Infused

Infused

MY STORY OF CANCER, HOPE AND LOVE

COURTNEY BAX LASATER

Acadian House
PUBLISHING
Lafayette, Louisiana

The Acadian House Publishing Speakers Bureau can bring authors to your live event. For more information or to book an author, contact Acadian House Publishing at (337) 235-8851, Ext. 104, or info@acadianhouse.com.

ISBN 10: 0-925417-21-1
ISBN 13: 978-0-925417-21-3

♦ Published by Acadian House Publishing, Lafayette, Louisiana
  (Trent Angers and Darlene Smith, co-editors; pre-press production
  by Leah Ewing)
♦ Printed by Sheridan Books, Chelsea, Michigan

Courtney's song

In early July of 2016, Courtney Bax Lasater called our publishing house to ask if she could interest us in publishing her book, which was nearing completion.

She described the book as a unique look into a woman's journey through Cancerland – up close and personal, frank, to-the-point and spiced with an extra dose of sarcasm. She noted that she was born sarcastic and had sharpened this talent in night school (read, *Saturday Night Live*).

A week or so later, we received her pitch letter:

"I was diagnosed with breast cancer at age 30 and was later re-diagnosed with Stage 4 metastatic cancer. I have chronicled my journey from fighter to survivor to 'lifer,' and would love the opportunity to share it with others – not only for the camaraderie of others facing this diagnosis but also to assist the caregivers in navigating this bumpy road."

She sent us several chapters to read. We were touched by her story and enamored of her lively, entertaining writing style.

We were moving closer to green-lighting her project when a call came into our office a few months later, in October, that stopped us in our tracks. Tearfully and in a halting voice, Courtney told us her doctor had given her only a week or 10 days to live. She repeated her request, that she really, really wanted us to publish her book.

"I wrote it to help others with cancer – and to leave a legacy for my little boy," she said, referring to her son, Evan, who was 18 months old at the time. "I want my son to know who I am."

Who could have said no to her request?

"Yes, Courtney, we will publish your story," we assured her.

Courtney started her book as a blog. It reads more or less like a diary – a chronological report, a step-by-step account of what she was experiencing. It's filled with riveting detail, valuable insights, touches of humor and, as she promised, that extra dose of sarcasm.

Notably, she wrote much of the book with what she called

"chemo brain" or "cancer brain," which, we understand, greatly diminishes one's ability to focus, to concentrate, to recall detail and nuance. Thus, as we see it, writing this much material with such clarity and wit was quite a feat.

Because of her great love of music, her original manuscript included lyrics to some of the songs that fed her soul. While the lyrics couldn't be included in this book, a list of the songs and their writers can be found on a playlist in the back of the book.

Several of these song titles, or a line or two from their lyrics, were used as chapter titles. But Courtney wanted to call them "tracks" instead of chapters – in keeping with her idea that they were part of the soundtrack of her life.

One of the tunes she mentions briefly in the body of the text is the theme song for the movie *Rocky*. Titled "Gonna Fly Now," it is a very inspiring song – sort of an anthem – that rallies the courage and resolve of a boxer who is facing seemingly impossible odds.

Courtney's story, too, is about a fighter who is deeply committed to going the distance.

– *Trent Angers,*
 Editor

Dedicated to
Roger, forever mi amor and my rock
and to
Evan, my greatest treasure

My journey thru Cancerland

My story is full of angels watching over me, both in Heaven and on Earth.

I really wouldn't have gone to the doctor. I'm nothing if not a "walk it off, slap 'em on the ass, and tell 'em good game" type of girl. I wouldn't have thought anything about it.

On our honeymoon a few months earlier, in March of 2011, my husband and I had decided to hire a personal trainer. I was scheduled for my annual medical exam, but for reasons unknown my doctor called to push it back two weeks. During that delay, my trainer had me doing exercises that used muscles I'd never worked before. As a result, I was really sore in places I didn't even know existed.

And that's when I found the lump.

Never an alarmist and perpetually dismissive, I thought it was nothing.

My husband, however, is not the dismissive type. Unlike me, he knew far too many people with cancer. So, I agreed to tell the doctor about the little lump in my armpit. I was going to be there anyway.

And besides, it's not like there was anything to it.

Now, I'm not a doctor. I never turned the pages of a medical textbook or sat through a lecture on cancer.

But, I have lived it.

Since the moment I heard the words, "You have cancer," I have lived the heartache, the pain and the roller coaster ride of both victory and defeat.

I still can't look at the photos of me that were taken over the Memorial Day weekend of 2011, out at Lake LBJ near our hometown of Austin. This was the weekend just before I got the bad news. I deleted these pictures from Facebook. I filed them away in a back corner of my mind. I hate those photos because there is an innocence in my eyes that is no longer there. It hurts too much to see the moment when my carefree spirit died.

This is just my story - filled with tears, joy, laughter, a few cuss words, and an extra helping of sarcasm - on how I navigated the world of cancer.

Will Rogers once said that there is no better exclamation point than a good "hell" or a "damn." Cancer has provided plenty of opportunity for exclamation points, as you will see on the following pages.

As the days turned into weeks and the weeks turned into years, I wrote down my thoughts about my journey through Cancerland.

This is my story:

Infused with chemotherapy,

infused with sarcasm,

infused with hope.

– *Courtney Bax Lasater*

Contents

Infused

'Ain't no place for the weary kind'

Despite my age and what we all thought was just a fibroid, the doctor pushed the envelope, following up the mammogram with a sonogram and ultimately a biopsy. The biopsy was super-fun – even more fun than squishing your boobs between two glass plates, if you can imagine anything more fun than that!

Maybe poking your eye with a fork.

Or smashing your finger with a hammer.

Or bending your fingernail in half right back to the pink part.

All these things were as fun as having some stranger manhandle your boobs and tell you to try to get closer to the glass because you don't have enough boobs to mash. *Thanks, jerk!*

The breast cancer biopsy was even more fun. This was like the Merry-go-Round of Suck – one glorious ride after another. It was like a spring-loaded shot, except when it sprang back it took your skin and your potential cancer with it. Because it was so much fun, once they got the potential cancer out they did it again and deposited a marker that would identify the tumor on the scans.

On June 2, 2011, a few days after the biopsy, I was driving to work when I got a call from the doctor's office. It was the nurse. She said the doctor wanted me to come in.

"Mrs. Lasater, the doctor would like to see you."

In that moment, time stood still. Other drivers zoomed past, completely oblivious to the fact that in that moment, at that stop light, at the intersection of FM 620 and 2222, my world was falling out from beneath me. It was my "Where were you when President Kennedy was shot?" moment. It felt like being underwater. The clicking of the turn signal and the song on the radio all played in a muffled roar.

There I was in my car being forced to turn left by the voice on the other end of the phone instead of continuing to work.

There I was at the fork in the road, standing between the life I had planned for myself and the life that was planned for me.

"So, it's cancer?" I asked anxiously.

"She would like for you to come in and meet with her."

"So... it's cancer?" I repeated.

"Mrs. Lasater, I cannot say, but she'd like for you to come in as soon as you can."

"OK, well, then it's cancer," I concluded.

I'm not sure why being declared victor in this verbal sparring match was relevant. If I was right, it meant that I was 30 years old, a newlywed, and I had cancer. If I was right, our new duo had become a trio, with cancer singing harmony.

The next two calls were to my husband and to my parents. Everyone was in disbelief. We were convinced this was some insurance ploy to collect yet another premium or two. Husband told me to wait in the car until he could get there. For once, I did as I was told, knowing that what lies before me would surely change our lives.

It's never a good sign when your doctor can't look you in the eye because she is in tears. She gave us the news and had already set up an appointment with an oncologist. Looking back, I'm so thankful for that move on her part. It helped us to start moving forward instead of standing still in disbelief.

This oncologist was able to answer a lot of our questions and help us clear a path through the forest of the unknown.

Upon my diagnosis, the doctor handed me a bag from the Breast Cancer Resource Center of Austin. This bag and this amazing organization became my lifeline – that is, until Duke, the Wonder Dog, Husband's yellow lab, decided it looked like a nice appetizer. The bag contained a wealth of information, including a book full of questions to ask the doctors and a brochure about the Pink Ribbon Cowgirls – a support group for women in my area under 40 years old who were diagnosed with breast cancer. These women had walked in my shoes. They had heard the same three words I had – "You have cancer" – and had felt the earth move under their feet. They became the greatest sorority you never wanted to join.

We began shopping once I secured my second bag and book from the Breast Cancer Resource Center. Ever the one to appreciate a great pair of shoes, handbag or cute outfit just to lounge around the house, I found that this kind of shopping wasn't all it was cracked up to be.

And so it began – the arduous task of shopping for a doctor, a doctor who was supposed to save my life. No pressure.

With each day and every appointment, we received more and more calls and texts. All of our loved ones wanted to know what came next. We were exhausted from the all-day meetings, tired of explaining and re-explaining what had happened. We loved that our friends and family wanted to show they cared, but this meant we had to keep re-living the heartache each time we told another person. Every time we told someone the latest news, it became harder and harder to deny our reality. It was the gift that kept on giving. A friend suggested a Caring Bridge blog to keep everyone updated. So I started writing. It provided both an outlet for my emotions and a one-stop shop for friends and loved ones to keep tabs.

The next few weeks were a blur. We started driving up and

down I-35, shopping for a doctor, comparing opinions, treatment options and the like. Married for only three months, all of a sudden we faced so many decisions. Which doctor do I use? What if one could save my life and the other couldn't? Do I need radiation? Which chemo regimen do I choose? Do I do a lumpectomy or mastectomy? Do I save the nipples? Would I lose my hair?

All were questions that, looking back, seemed trivial but were anything but at the time. It was our honeymoon year, and I had no idea if I would even slightly resemble the woman that Husband married. Would he still love me? Would he stay?

Should I let him bow out gracefully? How ironclad was that return policy?

Oh, and by the way, will I live?

This was the tornado of questions whirling around my mind at all hours of the day and night as Dr. Google and I teamed up in an effort to save my life.

* * * * *

I was sitting in a desolate, sterile hallway, swimming in my stylish new ensemble – an understated blue and green paper gown and matching pants big enough for three. I felt like I was *Laugh-In's* Edith Ann – the little girl in the big chair, in a world way too big – as I nervously kicked my legs back and forth under the bench. I was frozen, watching all these other people dying with cancer, most of them two to three times older than I, being wheeled by from scan to scan on stretchers. Meanwhile, I quietly hummed "One of these things is not like the other one," wondering, *How in the hell did I get here?*

It was a grueling all-day scan day – a sick and twisted version of Sunday Funday, where instead of bottomless mimosas, I ingested countless radioactive cocktails while wondering if my nightmare could get even worse. My entourage wasn't amused. I guess the cocktails in the waiting room were even worse than the ones in the back hallways of the hospital. Either that or Dad had gotten tired of small talk.

It's been said that I'm my father's daughter. We're not really in for chit-chat for the sake of chit-chat, particularly during stressful times. Leave us alone with our habit of internalizing our feelings while we formulate a plan. We didn't really need to hash it out with anyone. We'd let you know if you were needed.

I remember lying on the skinny little table during the bone scan watching the screen above me pixelate with little dots, identifying anything that might be cancer. Was every dot cancer? What were the bright spots? My heart raced and panic ensued. I lay there making deals with The Man Upstairs. I remember praying that it wouldn't get worse, pleading my case that if it was contained I promised to have a good attitude and take this challenge head on.

Ever one to ask questions even in times of duress, I had a great conversation with the tech about the technology and how it worked and how they managed to get some people on this sleek little thing that I was barely teetering on.

In a previous life, I wanted to be a biochemist. I found DNA and genetics and everything about science fascinating. I subscribed to all sorts of nerd magazines and read them cover to cover. If someone hadn't pointed out that my gregarious nature and hatred of math would be huge obstacles to this career path, I would have found myself in the medical field. (Cue Alanis Morrisette's *Ironic*.)

I was now thrust full force into the medical field without the benefits of the paycheck. Though being the patient wasn't exactly fun, the inner nerd in me was geeking out on how all of these things worked. If I had to be there, I was at least going to learn a few things.

Later in the day, I found myself face down headed into

another scan tunnel, with perfect little cut-outs just for my boobs. How quaint. As I tried to lie still, my nose started running and then the floodgates opened as I began sobbing. Part of it was sheer gravity. Part of it was the silence afforded me in the small examining room. Part of me was freezing from the temperature. But lastly, the biggest part of me was angry at the machine telling me to hold my breath on demand, frustrated at the compromising position I was in.

The technician stopped the scan and came and sat on the table with me. She held me and let me cry. She understood. She was a recent ovarian cancer survivor.

At the end of the day, I had been poked and prodded, stuck and x-rayed and pushed into tunnels and then poked and prodded some more. I had green dyes, purple dyes and yellow dyes injected into my body. They gave me a card for my purse that said I was radioactive – in the event I was arrested by airport police. I would have hated for them to think I was a terrorist because of the rainbow of radioactive material pulsing through my veins.

*   *   *   *   *

A few days later, we went to Dallas for the Sentinel Lymph Node Biopsy. The day started with more radioactive dye being injected into my breast. *Lucky color blue, come on down!* The tech said it would just be a quick prick and a burn. Sure, that was true if by "burn" she meant I'd feel inclined to stop, drop and roll because I was being consumed by flames. *Honey, clearly this wasn't one of those things they made you practice on each other in nursing school.*

The radioactive dye would settle in spots where cancer may have spread from my breast. The tech used a wand that looked like a miniature metal-detector to see where the dye had settled.

The dye settled into four lymph nodes, with one testing positive for cancer. Dr. A said this was good news. But the concept of things being deemed "good news" simply because they could have been worse was already starting to wear thin.

With no guidance from anyone in the medical profession, I made the decision to have a single-side mastectomy. I wanted the cancer out of my body as fast as possible. At the time, I thought I'd save the right side for potential children.

That was the end of my say in the matter. Because of my age, chemotherapy was in my future whether I liked it or not.

* * * * *

With nothing left to do but wait, we headed to Las Vegas. We had previously made plans to go to Vegas for a few days with Husband's family.

Though this 8.5 magnitude earthquake had split open the world beneath my feet, there wasn't a lot we could do at the time to get to the other side. We might as well attempt to have a good time. And besides, it would be my first chance to flash my fancy implant card at the airport when they deemed I looked suspicious, or radioactive, or suspicious and radioactive.

The first night in Vegas we went to see the Beatles' "Love." I remember sitting in the dark, sipping on my cocktail of choice – Grey Goose and tonic with a bunch of lime – with tears streaming down my face. It was the first time since "it" happened that I had a chance to be alone with my thoughts. When the words to "Blackbird" came streaming through the speakers, the floodgates opened yet again: *Blackbird singing in the dead of night; take these broken wings and learn to fly.*

I was jolted back to reality by the sounds of my father-in-law snoring and Husband bumping me on the arm, asking me when the singers were going to come out. Apparently, no one had told him what *Cirque du Soleil* meant. He thought we were going to a concert. *Sorry, Husband. You just get to watch these dancing acrobats in spandex jump around on trampolines to a Beatles' soundtrack for the next hour. My mistake.*

When we returned from Vegas, I had a few days before my surgery. I don't know what came over me, but I called our wedding photographer who had also become a friend. I told her I needed her as soon as possible. I asked her if she wouldn't mind taking some photos of me. I wasn't trying to make some racy Valentine's Day gift for Husband. I wasn't even sure he'd ever see them. The photos were for me. I just wanted some sort of proof of what I looked like before, of the woman I was before cancer, in the event it all went to hell.

What would I look like? Would I be all mangled and scarred?

Would I still feel like a woman?

At least this way I'd have something to remember my former self by if I wanted to.

She didn't ask questions. She didn't charge me. She knew what these photos meant to me.

*   *   *   *   *

The day of the mastectomy started just like any other day, but with a red Sharpie in hand. I had Husband write "yours" and "mine" on my bad and good boob, respectively. We had all heard about those times when they switched the baby in the hospital. Not this girl!

The night before, I managed to pack enough clothes for two weeks in the hospital. I could not make a decision to save my life, and I spent about 45 minutes painting and repainting my toenails different colors. The mundane tasks offered some respite from the unknown that lay before me.

We headed out the door Wednesday, with red Sharpie

writing on my boobs and hot pink polish on my toes. An invigorating game of "I spy" ensued for the drive from Austin to Dallas. This was a great distraction, but it didn't dissolve the fears pulsing through my veins.

These long drives to Dallas were quickly showing us newlyweds how each other coped with stress. While I wanted to sit in silence and internalize while I planned my attack, Husband became a Chatty Cathy on a Pixie Stick sugar rush. While other newlyweds our age battled over who did the dishes and the laundry, Husband and I were thrust full force into the trials and tribulations of couples married for 35 years or more. On more than one occasion, Husband thought I had a negative attitude when all I wanted to know was what kind of battle should I prepare for? He was going to wing it with his positive attitude, but I was going to come in armed and dangerous – ready for whatever this asshole cancer was going to throw at me.

When we arrived, they took me to the holding area to change and consult with each of the doctors prior to surgery. It was here that I had a bit of a meltdown with my parents. All this focus on cancer the past few weeks and it was only then that it dawned on me that this was a really big surgery.

Dr. B was the first to get to inspect the artwork on my boobs. He wasn't even mildly amused. In his defense, he was already a little leery of Husband. On several consultation appointments leading up to this day, Dr. B walked into the examination room to find Husband funneling his nervous energy by juggling the sample implants or using them as stress balls.

After four hours of surgery, with the oncologist and plastic surgeon working together, I was able to see visitors. As expected, I promptly did my makeup and brushed my hair. I was in good spirits and felt like a champ, but that may have had something to do with the copious amounts of pain meds I had running through my IV.

The following day, they finally let me out of bed. I felt like I had a football shoved underneath the skin of my chest. The most painful part was the *latissimus dorsi* flap part of the surgery. They had removed the breast tissue and the three or four questionable lymph nodes. They cut my back and took part of the *latissimus* muscle and dragged it around to the front of my chest as a cup holder for my new tissue expander. This resulted in a great party trick of being able to move my boob toward my back with any use of my tricep.

The tissue expander is a saline-filled sack with a port that is used to stretch the tissue for the breast implant. It is slowly filled up over time to the desired size until it is eventually replaced with implants.

Once I was able to go home, it took some time to figure out how to sleep and dress with this football in my chest on one side and a normal sized boob on the other. I started to re-think my decision not to take the other boob at the same time. Who did I let talk me into this? *Oh, wait. That was me – the one with the counterfeit medical degree.*

I had had surgery on a Friday. Because of the nature of my job, my "weekend" landed on Mondays and Tuesdays. On Wednesday, I was back at work. With no prior experience of having a mastectomy, I was unsure how long I would be out of work and had inquired about short-term disability before my surgery. My Human Resources contact was adamant that I was not allowed to be out more than seven days without taking disability.

How was it relevant to her? What if I had simply chosen to zero-out my vacation with a boob job or nose job? Why was she suddenly so involved?

She pushed for a return-to-work date. She needed me to commit to when I would be back at work, or I would have to take disability.

I was frustrated and angry. I didn't have a normal job where disability was a simple W-2 calculation. Filing for disability meant I would be walking away from hard-earned commissions. It takes months to see a paycheck in real estate. It is the most anticlimactic commission job in the world. You sell a home and then eight months later money shows up. I had no idea how long I'd be out. I had never done this before.

Where was her compassion? She was just pushing papers and checking boxes. Her attitude compounded the stress of the procedure. Not only did I have to face a cancer diagnosis at 30 and come to terms with losing my hair and never physically looking the same again, I also had this Human Resources bird sitting on my shoulder, pecking at me to heal according to her available check boxes.

At 10:05 on the Wednesday following my surgery, I received a call on my office line from H.R.

"I just wanted to make sure you were in your chair," she said.

Come again? My blood began to boil as I thought of all the creative expletives I'd hurl in her direction as soon as I could get off the phone. *Yes, my swollen sore body that had been split open and had tubes connected to it collecting fluid was "in my chair." Thank you, Captain Sensitive.*

The body drains fluid after surgery. I didn't know that. I had two drains, each about two feet long, coming out of my body, with these huge bulbs on the end to collect the fluid generated from the tissue removal. It was difficult to navigate around the drains. Getting dressed was difficult. Lying in bed or on the couch was cumbersome. The drains would get tangled or begin to weigh me down as they became full. I wasn't exactly the picture of sex appeal while dragging around these drains full of fluids. When I'd take a shower, I'd wrap them around my neck to keep gravity from pulling them down. Inevitably, I'd forget they were there and get them caught on something, thereby causing gut-wrenching pain.

Fortunately, a local Austinite and fellow breast cancer survivor, Cheri Mathews, was working on the patent for a shirt, called Heal in Comfort, that held the drains. She wanted the shirt to be standard issue at hospitals for those undergoing a mastectomy or heart surgery, etc. She had partnered with the Breast Cancer Resource Center in Austin, so I was able to get one of the prototypes. That shirt became my uniform. It had a place for my drains and Velcro up the center.

Husband helped me drain and measure the fluid each day until I grew tired of this and decided there was no harm in fudging on the drainage report. In my mind, the sooner the draining stopped, the sooner I could get those tubes and drains pulled out of my side. As it turned out, this was not advisable. Dr. B did in fact remove the tubes, one at a time over the course of two weeks, but my little fib led to my sitting up in bed one night only to find I had sprung a leak.

Days later, we received the preliminary pathology results. That was when I went from Average Joe to Doogie Howser, M.D. overnight. ER, PR, HER2, high proliferation: All these terms were thrown around nonchalantly by doctors, like I knew what in the hell they were talking about. These terms told us if the cancer was fed by estrogen or progesterone, if it had HER2 protein, and how quickly the cells were dividing.

Things were happening too quickly for me to grasp these terms. I couldn't type fast enough to get these answers through Google, and the doctor-speak was overwhelming. Pretty much everything that had been said since the moment I heard "You have cancer" sounded like the teacher on Charlie Brown, "*Wa wa wa wa wa wa.*"

Doctor appointments were fruitless - well, not fruitless in some ways, but I was M.I.A. I'm not sure why I was even there. Could I have a designated hitter? It was what I imagined it would feel like if I had lost my hearing. There was this constant ringing in my ears, a pounding that would never stop. I could hear the sound of my heartbeat louder than any other sounds. It was deafening. It was simultaneously deafening and eerily quiet. I felt like a bystander in my own life. The doctor would say something that would send my brain off on a rabbit trail. This was when we learned to either write notes or secretly record all of our visits so that when I snapped back into what was my new reality, I could feign some attempt at being an active participant. No one seemed to understand: I didn't want to be an active participant in this terrible story.

On top of this, everyone was crying. Everyone around me was crying and hugging on me. I should have prefaced this with the fact that I'm not an overly emotional person. I don't have highs or lows. I have blips. I think Husband would begrudgingly concur that I'm the man in our house because I'm perfectly comfortable with silence and not talking about my emotions. This is a particularly good trait in my occupation where in negotiations he who speaks first loses.

Being thrust into this situation felt like an out-of-body experience, watching all these people crying. I kept thinking, *What in the hell are you people doing? How am I supposed to get it together if you can't get it together! Get your shit together! Come on. I don't have time to give you a pep talk! Stop hugging me. Go to your corner.*

I later read about "The Ring Theory" as a way of coping with grief. It was advice that I wish I had had before that very moment when I was wearing my emotions on my face, looking at everyone around me like they were a bunch of unicorns. The Ring Theory involves concentric circles. The person at the center of the trauma is in the center circle. The next closest person is in the next circle and so on. The rule is comfort in/dump out. Only positive and encouraging things can be said to the person in a smaller circle. Negative comments can be made only to people in a larger circle. *Go complain about how unfair this is to someone else! I have shit to do. We're in action mode. Emotions can come later.*

* * * * *

This surgery wasn't the end of the Edward Scissorhands bonsai-sculpting on this journey. It was just the start of things that would involve 20 operations and/or procedures.

Nipples, nipples, nipples.

There, I said it. Let the awkwardness settle in. This story is about breast cancer. Boobs and nipples are the lead actors. My skin wouldn't cooperate and The Dynamic Surgeon Duo's attempt at a nipple-sparing surgery was for naught. My skin kept dying and wouldn't regenerate. In order to start chemotherapy, I couldn't have any infection or weakened immunity, so they cut out all of the dead or dying tissue and took some skin from my pelvic area to backfill this now non-existent nipple.

To add insult to injury, this poorly timed surgery happened the day I was supposed to be on a girls' trip to Napa. Change of plans: Instead of sipping fine wine with my pals, I was enjoying a full-bodied, woodsy aroma anesthesia cocktail. I'm still a little bitter they didn't at least bring me back a bottle of wine from this non-refundable trip. At least I still have all of my front teeth; I can't say the same for all the girls on the trip. I hear fun was had by all!

After this surgery, I detoured to the wig store to have a little fun with my hair's impending doom. It's funny how life is. I remembered, years before, one of the ladies at work had gotten breast cancer. I was young and inquisitive. One day I was in her office asking about her situation, and I remember telling her that if I ever got cancer I'd get wigs of all different colors and try to have fun with it. Well, here it was. The Man Upstairs was calling my bluff. The time was now. *Prove it, Courtney.*

And I was going to hold true to my word.

S.O.B., this can't be me!

We were back at it again, doctor-shopping.

On a referral, we met with Dr. X., who was supposed to be one of the best.

The best what? The doctor with the best bedside manner? The best researcher? Who deemed her the best and on what graduated scale?

Anyway, she was the first doctor to see the full pathology of my cancer, the first to know what really lies before us.

Cancer is serious, and I didn't need someone just to tell me what I wanted to hear. But I thought that in the oncology field, a course in bedside manners or a slight semblance of a soul would have been nice. But, no, on the contrary, it turns out that is not a prerequisite at all.

It took less than three minutes for Dr. X to stab me through the heart and twist the knife. She was nothing if not efficient.

"Oh... you have such nice, long, thick, pretty hair. It is going to take you *foreeeever* to grow it back," she observed.

No kidding, really?

Her comment sent me into a tailspin. I decided to try to rejoin the conversation right about the inopportune time that she added another zinger:

"It's not a matter of *if* this cancer is going to kill you. It's just a matter of *when*."

Son-of-a-bitch. OK, you little troll. Now you're playing dirty.

29

Everything she was saying was the opposite of what all the other doctors had told us. All the other doctors had told me, "It will just be a year of your life," yet here she was talking about my dying.

Was she full of it – or did she see something they didn't since she was looking at the actual pathology?

With my thoughts spiraling out of control, I somehow managed to get out a question about family planning. After all, we had just gotten married and hoped to have a future to plan after this quaint little detour through Hell. Dr. X replied that I should be more concerned about whether I was even going to make it at all rather than with planning a future – much less one with children.

What? Even going to make it! Where did that come from?

She was, however, super-excited about how healthy I was. This astute observation led her to announce that I was ideal for her experimental trials.

Experimental trials? I only had Stage 2 cancer!

I thought trials meant there weren't other options. What happened to all the other treatments that came before last-ditch-effort clinical trials? I needed to check my ticket. I must have boarded the wrong plane.

She put us in this room at a small round table and nonchalantly slid forms in front of me that seemed to say I agreed to enroll in available trials. I was going through the motions and signing things I wasn't even reading. I couldn't comprehend what was happening.

Son-of-a-bitch! Other than this whole cancer thing, I was the picture of perfect health. Anything positive we had heard to date from other doctors was kiboshed by this little hobbit. It was horrid. I felt like someone was holding my head under water while I was trying to come up for air. I was just drowning in devastation.

Up until this moment, I had been pretty strong. When she

left the room, I collapsed in Husband's arms, and he literally carried me out to the car, where we called Dr. A. It was after hours, but he graciously invited us to meet him. We went to his office, and he tried to dispel the fears instilled in us by the troll.

"It'll be only a year of your life," he kept saying.

Despite his efforts, we drove home to Austin in silence, in a state of disbelief.

* * * * *

With a few surgeries behind me, I still had to find an oncologist.

The one I met with the day I was diagnosed was great, but I was unsure whether her facility had access to all the best options. It turned out that she disagreed with the way Dr. A did my mastectomy, and they had a heated discussion about surgical techniques.

Well, that's just great! It hadn't dawned on me that there might be a right way and a wrong way to go about this.

Why did I have to sort through all of this? I had a job. I wasn't trying to pull double duty. That was their job! Everyone seemed to be recommending the same treatment regimens – Four Adriamycin/Cytoxan (A/C) infusions plus 12 Taxol infusions. I could do it all in six, but I naively wanted to maintain some semblance of a normal life. A/C is cancer-speak for "This is going to suck." It is affectionately called the Red Devil and is the culprit behind the dreaded hair loss that would cause me to lose my "nice *loooong*, thick hair."

While all the doctors were on the same page regarding chemotherapy, no one would weigh in on radiation. I had one positive lymph node. Textbook procedures said I should remove 22 lymph nodes. More modern discussions said it was an unnecessary risk for lymphedema. No one would put his or her practice on the line to give me a real opinion. It was incredibly frustrating; I got answers that weren't answers just so they could cover their asses. This was my life we were talking about. Within reason, the doctors usually approved the crapshoot of decisions we non-medical types made.

We met with a radiation oncologist in hopes that someone would grow a pair and help us make a decision. His advice:

"If it was my wife, I'd tell her to do radiation, but if she said no, I wouldn't lose sleep over it."

Thank you for your totally useless non-opinion opinion. I could find that type of advice on Wikipedia!

After consulting a slew of physicians, and, of course, Dr. X, the head hobbit, we made the decision to opt out of radiation for fear of lymphedema and potential heart damage. It was a decision that could change my life forever. It could mean the beginning of the end. Yet, no one who was in a position to know would weigh in. Since the treatment recommendations were the same, we chose the doctor closest to home to simplify our now-chaotic lives.

With a chance to bob our heads above water to get a little air, we decided to look into the fertility options. Most of the doctors said we shouldn't even need to be concerned about this. They said I should be fine after chemo. But we weren't ready to gamble our future away on a hope and a prayer. We were short on time. I had only a few weeks before starting chemo. With our regularly scheduled six-hour round trip to Dallas as our only free time, I started my Google search for local fertility doctors.

The plan was to fertilize and freeze embryos, in case chemo wrecked my ability to bear a child. I made an appointment with one of the fertility doctors in town who was supposed to be the best. The soonest she could get us in was a week later. The clock ticked on.

We met with her and explained how time-sensitive our

situation was. She knew the drop-dead date when I had to start chemotherapy. She said her office could accommodate this and escorted my husband down the hall to start the process.

A week later, I called repeatedly to try to move the process forward, but to no avail. I couldn't get anyone to call me back. When my incessant calls finally got through to a live person, she confessed their lab would be closed for two weeks so we'd need to schedule some time after that.

I didn't have this imaginary "time after that." *It was now or never.* Why couldn't they understand that we either did this now or we didn't do it at all? The latter might mean we'd never have children. How was this happening?

In the midst of this whole shit show, I turned 31 years old, and the day passed without celebration.

We started scrambling. We were so angry, but we didn't have time to do anything except act. Husband came unglued and got very upset with the doctor – which was quite comical from my vantage point. I was usually the one who didn't shy away from confrontation. Husband, as noted previously, was Polly Positive. Nothing got under his skin. His fury was justified when you considered the tight spot we were in. Time was a luxury we didn't have. This had been carefully explained.

So, we contacted another, newer facility and they understood the urgency. The doctor's mother was a cancer survivor so he understood what we were going through. They rushed us in and started the process. We sat at a little table in the corner, and they taught us how to inject me with cancer-feeding hormones to stimulate egg production for harvest. (It was here that I realized I hadn't paid nearly enough attention in health class. I apparently had little more than a rudimentary knowledge of how babies were actually made.)

We found ourselves in the all-too-familiar place of filling out forms. What did we want to do with the embryos if we never used them? Would we donate them to science? Would we donate them to another couple? Would we destroy them?

Hell if I knew! I still hadn't figured out how we had traveled so quickly from picking out wedding flowers and cakes to how we were going to save my life. We were time-traveling in reverse! We were making decisions now that we shouldn't have to make for years, or even at all.

This little baby-making adventure wasn't going to be cheap. This "just in case" insurance policy would be expensive. We fell in the socioeconomic class in which we made enough money that we didn't qualify for any financial assistance, but we didn't make enough that this was going to be just a drop in the bucket.

But children were a big part of our life plan. We were not ready to surrender all decisions to cancer.

This doctor advised me to get Lupron shots every three months during chemotherapy to protect my ovaries. This was the very first time anyone had mentioned this. We didn't know what we didn't know. This should have been standard advice when a woman in her reproductive years was diagnosed with cancer, but it was not. There should have been a manual, but there was not. It should have been outlined in a neat little flow chart. *If this, then you do this. If you're under 50 years old and you haven't gone through menopause, then do this.*

Where was this handy dandy cheat sheet? The doctor explained that the chemicals in chemotherapy go to the most active cells – cancer, hair and ovaries. For a disease that had been around for a long time, there seemed to be quite a few loose ends. The Lupron shots would suppress the ovaries and try to keep the chemicals from going there in hopes that I could have children naturally at a later date. It was good that we stumbled across this information.

The time crunch meant our regularly scheduled activities were a moot point. These injections were time-sensitive and had to be done as prescribed. But still, it was terrifying for me to inject myself full of hormones – the very thing that fed my cancer. We kept telling ourselves the chemotherapy would hopefully undo any of the damage we were doing.

We showed up before dawn for the egg harvest. The building was freezing. I suppose all the "males" and "females" needed to stay cold for transfer.

Once again, I had to answer a thousand questions from the nurse. They were questions I had answered *ad nauseam* for three months. Surely, someone had been writing this down. How many different ways could I answer the same questions? How old was I when I started my period? Had I ever taken birth control pills? How did I find the lump?

I was too young to have had a mammogram. I showed her where I found the lump.

"Yup. Tons of our patients find it in the armpit," she said.

I was positive the breast self-exam shower-hanger in the college dorms did not show anything beyond the circular pattern of the fingers moving on the boob. Does anyone ever consult the nurses before writing these helpful little instruction cards?

She continued asking about my health and what other health issues I had.

I laughed. Other than the cancer, I was the picture of perfect health.

With the repetition of this barrage of questions, I was becoming increasingly aware that the medical community didn't seem to know their ass from their elbow. They agreed that an early menstrual cycle could contribute to a breast cancer diagnosis. But from there, the theories fell apart at the seams.

Maybe it was my age, but even medical professionals seemed to focus on genetics though only five to ten percent of breast cancers were hereditary. Nothing about this was genetics. Five different tests said that I had no genetic predisposition to cancer. I was just that lucky.

After all was said and done, we harvested seven eggs with

seven resulting embryos. We were officially parents of septup-lets.

Kids – check. Now, on to chemotherapy. I had run out of ways to procrastinate.

It had been just over two months since I was diagnosed with cancer. It was time for me to go to the blue chair.

The land of blue chairs

L et's talk about the chair and the teacher who instructed me on how to use it.

But first, a word about the other crappy teachers I had in my pre-college days.

There was the teacher I blamed for my lack of math skills, the one who spent my entire eighth grade year teaching me Base Five - a way to count in the event that I didn't have fingers. She was followed quickly by an irate Iranian algebra teacher who would scream hysterically if you asked questions. Then there was the history teacher who spent an entire semester letting us build forts in the woods; this happened to be a pivotal year in my history schooling and could explain my utter lack of knowledge of anything past the Civil War. I had a chemistry teacher who used to let us break thermometers and play with the mercury balls or set ink pens on fire and watch them drip fire.

Now, flash forward to 2011 and my class called Chemotherapy 101. Husband and I showed up for orientation a few days before the start of my infusions, and we met the person I'll refer to as my teacher.

I don't know if we ended up with a substitute that day or if this moron was normally the teacher, but she put us in this huge conference room and pulled up a chair right next to me. She completely invaded my personal space. She proceeded to describe the crap that would be my life for the next six months. She repeated over and over how much crap would be involved.

Because she apparently ran out of material to fill her allotted class time, she thought we should test-drive "the chair." Was she kidding me? This was like asking someone on death row if he wanted to test-drive the electric chair, you know, just to get comfortable with the idea.

So, she walked us into the infusion room, filled with people who looked like they were on their deathbeds, most sleeping after their Benadryl infusions. That may have been normal to her, but I was unable to conceal the look of disbelief on my face. She sat each of us down in a blue infusion chair. She gave us headphones and a TV remote then pressed "play" on a video that should have been named "Suck."

This little movie won't win any Academy Awards. It was interview after interview with cancer patients talking about side effects: vomiting, nausea, fatigue, diarrhea.

Tell me again, why was I watching this? I started crying. I knew this was going to suck. I didn't need to read books or watch movies or talk about the severity of how much it would suck. But I didn't have a choice. There was no opt-out button. Trust me, I looked for one.

As we walked out of this sick and twisted movie theater, I saw a woman my age checking in, wearing a cute little workout outfit, a bandana and big hoop earrings. Somehow she made having cancer and being bald look cute and stylish. I needed to know this person. She gave me the encouragement I needed. I didn't have to look all sad and depressed like the cast in the video. I could still find a way to be me, hair or no hair.

* * * * *

Before I could begin with the infusions, I had to meet a

few prerequisites. I had another surgery to install my port for chemotherapy. Acting as an artificial vein, the port is a device typically placed in the chest. It allows the medicine to be delivered directly into the bloodstream and spares your veins repeated injections of chemo.

I bled all over the bed when the nurse tried to start my IV. With little to laugh about in Cancerland, this would be one of my few sources of entertainment. Nurses would scramble around trying to stop the bleeding. I would warn them beforehand that I was going to bleed all over everything, often to no avail.

Next, I had a PET (Positron Emission Tomography) scan. I had received no information about this prior to my arrival. Apparently this scan uses a radiotracer to tag to glucose injected into the bloodstream. The radiotracer goes to the areas that use glucose the most. Cancer uses glucose differently, so it lights up on the scan.

In exchange for my name, the registrar handed me a cup full of barium, which tastes like a combination of orange juice and sunscreen lotion. Because one glass was so delightful, they handed me another. They took me to what looked like a bloodmobile in the parking lot, where they injected me with more radioactive material and instructed me to sit still in the dark for 45 minutes.

Tick tock. Tick tock. Tick tock. Tick tock.

When it was time for the scan, they handed me another glass of sunscreen to drink. The radioactive material they injected gave me the sensation that I needed a detour to the adult diaper aisle. There was a brief moment of self-doubt as I tried to determine if I had actually had an accident.

The next prerequisite was a MUGA test, which would get a baseline reading of the efficiency of my heart. I had entered the portion of the commercial where they rattled off all the terrifying side effects. "This drug is used to treat depression, but it may cause suicidal thoughts."

Wait! What? Am I the only one who heard that? Apparently, Adriamycin took a toll on the heart so they needed a baseline.

At the onset of any of these tests or scans, they did a saline flush of the IV. The saline flush tasted like burnt skunk, I had no prior experience with skunk – burnt or otherwise – but there was no other way to describe the horrific taste. In an era when Walgreen's could flavor any medication to taste like bubblegum upon request, this clearly had been overlooked. Because it didn't go into your mouth, no one had thought to add a little flavor to this beauty. (Side note: Peppermint candies take care of this issue extremely well. Husband became the peppermint go-to guy for all infusions going forward once we learned this from an amazing nurse.)

I had received a lot of these over the last month and my veins were sore, so I asked the technologist to use a different vein. He nodded and proceeded to use the same vein. To add insult to injury, he couldn't get it to work so he kept moving the needle around while it was still inside my vein. Back and forth. Back and forth.

No, that didn't hurt at all.

I eventually passed the prerequisites to start chemotherapy. It's funny how your perspective changes once you're waist-deep in Cancerland. The nurse called me with the scan results, rattling off information about cysts and kidney stones and venous malformations.

Yea, yea, yea. I really don't care, lady. Do I have any more cancer?

* * * * *

The week I started chemo, I proactively cut my hair into a bob, hoping it would lessen the trauma of being completely bald. Years of long ponytails were gone in the blink of an eye, swept up into a ball the size of a small animal. I also went for a final checkup with the plastic surgeon, who proceeded to inflate the tissue expander. This was the strangest experience. I was lying in a chair similar to one in a dentist office looking down at my chest as it slowly got larger and larger. I glanced over at Husband to see Operation Shock and Awe. It's highly likely that he made an inappropriate comment.

The final day before chemo, we went zip lining with Husband's family. This wasn't in my character as someone who, after a few first-hand experiences, was deemed unfit for rides in amusement parks. However, at this point I thought, *What the hell? What's the worst thing that could possibly happen?* I was preparing for the biggest roller coaster ride of my life. I might as well fly across the treetops of southwest Austin. My biggest concern was that I might get stuck in the middle of the line and have to pull myself to safety. Not only did I lack upper-body strength, I had just had several surgeries in my chest in a matter of two months. Luckily, it all worked out just fine.

With luggage in tow and no worse for wear, but a little sore, we arrived at the infusion center for the first of 16 treatments. We didn't know how long we'd be there or what we would need. Chemo 101 neglected to provide insight on any of this. A nurse escorted me to the chair, and in that moment I couldn't have been more thankful that I got to test-drive this chair previously. *Oh, wait! That wasn't true. It's sarcasm oozing from my veins.*

The nurses were amazing and walked me through everything that would happen. They started with a lot of premedication, including anti-nausea drugs, steroids and Benadryl, to try to mitigate any side effects.

It was a very long day. In addition to all the extra drugs to prevent any allergic reactions, the Adriamycin had to be hand-pushed instead of infused through an IV drip. Adriamycin is a vesicant chemical, meaning it can cause tissue damage if it escapes the vein. This is knowledge I could have done without, now that it was pumping through my veins.

That first chemotherapy went as well as could be expected. I found myself in bed for the remainder of the day having hot flash after hot flash as the medicine worked its way through my body. It may have been just in my mind, but it felt like I could almost trace its path through my body based on how it felt.

One treatment down in what would be seven months of chemotherapy.

With no doctor authorization, I decided to push the chemotherapy out of my body as quickly as possible. I downloaded an app on my phone that helped me track my water intake and I tried to drink 100 ounces a day. I took mineral baths to try to pull the toxins out of my body. I exercised. Some days, all I could do was walk around the block; other days, I would be back in the gym. Every day except infusion days I tried to do something physical to push myself and help my body heal. I sat in the steam room at my gym. Chemotherapy made it too hard for me to breathe in the dry air of the sauna. Breathing normally was already more difficult due to the effect of chemo on my red blood cells.

The Adriamycin infusions were every three weeks. It was on the third week that I felt the slicing pain begin. At first it felt like fine little slices from a paring knife. *Slice. Slice. Slice.* It started right on top. It moved on to a carving knife and then a chef's knife. *Slice. Slice. Slice.* Fine little slices, all over my head. This was what it felt like when my hair began to succumb to the chemotherapy.

Once my hair decided to leave the party, it threw up a peace sign and left. There was no long drawn out good-bye. This wasn't the phone conversation with the person who says good-bye and keeps talking, over and over again.

Hair was on my pillowcase when I woke up. Hair was on the shower floor. It was on the wall when I used the hair dryer. I even had to follow myself around with a vacuum!

One morning, after Husband went to play golf, I calmly walked into the bathroom and started shaving it off. I tied a section of it in a rubber band and saved it, not knowing in what color or texture my hair would come back. In that moment, though I was sad, I felt empowered. Watching each hair fall out one by one was traumatic. I was embarrassed about the mess I was making in the house. It was worse than what our German Shepherd did.

After months of my life spiraling out of control, taking my hair into my own hands gave me back some sense of control. It wasn't a pretty cut. It wasn't even and it was patchy, but I had done it myself. It didn't look that bad.

Husband was taken aback when he came home from golf to find me sporting a GI Jane haircut. He offered to help even it out, but evening out my butcher job required making it even shorter and shorter and shorter. At the sight of it, tears flowed down my face. Husband stood in horror, realizing that his good intentions had backfired.

* * * * *

As I found myself thrust into this world of cancer, I appreciated irony more and more.

Without fail, we'd ride the elevator down to the parking garage after chemo to find someone with an oxygen tank smoking a cigarette. It was like he had thrown up his hands and was saying, "Screw it! I already have cancer. I need a smoke break."

The conversations in my head provided constant entertainment. Though I had come out of the womb fluent in sarcasm, cancer had taken it to a new level. I stared at people in disbelief as they opened their mouths and said the dumbest things in an effort to comfort me when they found out I had cancer.

Without fail, both friends and strangers would tell me about people they knew who had cancer and later died. I knew they were trying to help, but I didn't need to bond with them over all the people they knew who didn't make it.

Thanks for your inspirational story. A simple "I'm sorry" would have sufficed.

Another common misconception was that this "free boob job" was cause for celebration. *Thank you for letting me know you thought my boobs were too small, but having all of your breast tissue and nipples removed and scars across your body is not a boob job.* A boob job is an elective surgery; a detour to the butcher shop is not. A boob job is something that you want to show off at the pool; this mangled mess of scars is not. And this is anything but free. What insurance pays for is quickly offset by unending physical costs like my hair and my energy.

They'd remind me that I was going to lose all my hair or that I could die. Or they'd just say "Ohhhh...." Initially, these comments infuriated me. When I realized that the stupidity wouldn't end anytime soon, I began playing a game in my head. I'd keep a tally of how long it would take until someone would say something stupid or insulting or what the most frequent idiotic comments were. It was a drinking game to keep my sanity, only without the buzz.

While I entertained myself, my body continued to go through the ups and downs of chemotherapy. With each treatment, the side effects worsened and my recovery time increased. It was taking longer and longer to bounce back.

On Adriamycin infusion days, I'd lie in bed all day until I could eventually get in the bathtub, where I'd fall asleep. I'd wake up shortly before drowning, crawl out of the tub, wrap myself in a towel and curl up in a ball on the bathmat. I didn't have the energy to get back into bed. I'd lie there and try to convince myself this chemotherapy wasn't killing me. Then Husband would find me and help me back to bed.

After finding me lying motionless on the floor a few times,

he routinely escorted me to the bedroom following each che-mo session. He wanted me to rest and not feel any pressure to do chores around the house. His great intentions, however, made me feel like I had been grounded, like I had been locked in a room with no access to the outside world.

By the end of the second day of treatment, I could walk to the end of the block. By the third day, I was back at work, going through the motions, but I couldn't make it a full day. By day four, I could make it through eight hours at the office as long as no one came in and required me to actually get out of my chair.

My neutrophil count continued to plummet. Neutrophils are a type of white blood cell that fights against infection. I was determined to soldier on. I made my way through infu-sion after infusion despite low red and white blood counts. Bone pain increased as a result of the low counts; my bones ached from my spine to the ends of my fingertips. It was dif-ficult stepping down from Husband's truck without feeling that I would collapse. I was determined to work through the pain without a Neulasta shot. This dreaded shot would boost my counts, but was notorious for the pain it caused. So, to stop my pain, I would have to cause significantly more pain.

Sleep was a figment of my imagination. I was always a light sleeper, but this had been taken to new heights. I could fall asleep, but I couldn't stay asleep. My brain bounced around from one thought to another like a ping pong ball. I could almost feel the train of thought jump across my brain. Little things like the light on the DVR woke me up and drove me mad. It was like closing my eyes while lying on the beach.

I was exasperated that this was not waking up Husband, too. Then again, not much woke him. I would be on my own if someone broke into the house. If sleep really corresponded to a clear conscience, he was in the clear.

Even after most of my eyelashes had left the building, I'd

wake up to the feeling of my one remaining eyelash flapping around in the wind from the fan. The exhaustion from sleep deprivation compounded the other side effects, making me very irritable.

The nurses helped me to stay ahead of the nausea, so I never got sick. Unfortunately, I made the mistake of eating a Jimmy John's meal and some pretzels during chemotherapy one day. While I managed to keep them down, I never ate during chemotherapy again.

You wouldn't believe the looks that patients would cut across the infusion room as one family member after another would bring food to their loved one.

Oh! Onions! You brought a food with tons of onions in it! That's so awesome that you wanted all of us to feel like we were eating with you! There must have been an approved food list, but then I supposed that varied from patient to patient. What made one patient nauseous made another feel better.

On top of the food lovers, there were the loud talkers. There were people who talked on their cell phones like there was no one else in the room. It was a lose-lose situation. No one wanted to be in this room and everyone was just trying to make the best of his or her own predicament. Surprisingly enough, this part of our journey made Husband and me more tolerant and accepting of others and what they may be going through.

Husband and I continued to spend our only days off together in the infusion room, returning to work each Wednesday. Both of us were selling houses at the time. Though it took the breath out of me, I'd climb the two flights of stairs each week to chemotherapy, simply in defiance of the limitations of cancer. Days turned into weeks and weeks turned into months as we counted down the 16 infusions.

With time, the people in the infusion room became like family, onions and all. We knew all the patients and the nurses.

I'd wheel myself around the infusion room to chat with others to pass the time. The nurses knew to come find me when my infusion alarm went off.

I always arrived at chemo in heels, looking perfectly healthy. There were even days when others would ask Husband what type of cancer he had, positive that I wasn't the patient. It was a combination of vanity and stubbornness. I had always dressed up. Husband knew me for four years before he realized my real height. I had worn heels everywhere before I had cancer. I had so little control left in my life. I'd be damned if cancer was going to take away my heels.

I made some great friends in the infusion room. Several of us saw the same oncologist and we would compare notes after our visits. We'd load the person up next for an appointment with any questions we had. Questions involved vitamins to follow-up testing to whether or not we should go to the dentist. We'd get different answers every time. One of us was told we could go to the dentist. The other was told absolutely not to go while we were in treatment. The discrepancies left us confused about what to do. Surely, the medical people knew we talked. We were trying to use this system to keep from calling the nurse line incessantly.

I completed the four Adriamycin treatments over 12 weeks. I then started the weekly Taxol infusions. Compared to Adriamycin, Taxol was a breath of fresh air for me. I started to crawl my way back into the land of the living. My stamina increased. I could actually run an errand or two after chemotherapy. The excitement of a glimpse of normalcy led to my overdoing it and recovery setbacks, but it was such a relief to feel like I was a part of society. My hair and eyebrows started to show signs of life as well.

While physically I felt like I could see my old self in the far-off distance, mentally I still couldn't even catch a glimpse of the old me. I finally convinced the doctor to take me off the steroids as I could tell they made me crazy and compounded my sleep issue. But still, normalcy was nowhere in sight.

I was riddled with guilt that for months Husband had carried the lion's share of responsibility – plus, he was with me for every doctor's appointment and infusion. He was taking an emotional beating from cancer and also having to keep our daily life afloat. I couldn't help with the yard or the laundry or any of the chores I had done before. It ate away at my pride to be so dependent on others.

I hated being the center of attention, the source of constant worry for others. I hated that our days off were spent in the infusion room or in doctor's appointments. When I would start to recover after each treatment, I caused my own setbacks in a fervent competition with myself to make up for the things I hadn't done the days before. I was my own worst enemy.

There was pressure to keep up appearances with our old social life, but my heart wasn't really in it. I still felt like crap, or just a slightly improved version thereof. I knew Husband needed the relief to get away from it all, so I would fake it and be social, but I wanted to stay in bed and watch mind-numbing marathon television. I wanted to see my friends, but I really wanted them to come to me.

* * * * *

With signs of improvement, everyone started talking about "beating cancer" and "when it is all behind us." I started to panic. My heart raced. What was next? What was going to happen when I was done with chemotherapy? While spending my days off anywhere other than the land of blue chairs sounded enticing, no treatment meant that nothing was fighting my cancer. What was to say it wouldn't come back?

Week after week, I continued with Taxol infusions. Taxol

can cause neuropathy, which basically is damage to your nerves, and neuropathy meant discontinued treatments. But I was determined to get every ounce of chemo prescribed.

In order to try to make it through all the chemo sessions, I started icing my hands and feet. It was miserable. The pain was intense. I wasn't made for the cold. I had to force myself to put my hands and feet in bags of ice. I didn't really know if there was any truth to it, but I heard that icing your extremities would constrict the blood vessels and keep the chemo from going into them and damaging nerve endings. I was willing to try anything to get each ounce of chemo the doctor prescribed.

My company, Taylor Morrison, honored me by coordinating a team for the Race for the Cure. It was an experience that I met with mixed emotions. I felt so honored and so loved that they would do that for me and that so many attended. However, I was exhausted by climbing the hills of downtown Austin with my diminished lung capacity and aching bones. But most of all, I was saddened. While thousands of people laughed and carried on in their funny coordinated pink outfits, shouting chants of victory and survival, I was fixated on the signs worn on the backs of those who walked in front of me – two tiny words, *In Memory.* Though thousands of others walked *In Honor of* those who made it, all I could see in the sea of pink was the very real possibility that this wasn't over.

* * * * *

As we neared the finish line of my 16 treatments, I dealt with my first cancer loss. She was friends with the well-accessorized woman we met at Chemo 101. Husband and I had had dinner with her and her family a few months before and I had just had lunch with her the previous week. And then she was gone.

I didn't know her well, but the loss shook me to the core. It also fueled the fear that had been bubbling up inside me as I got closer to completing chemotherapy: having nothing actively fighting my cancer.

My hair continued to grow back. Unfortunately, it grew from the back to the front. My eyelashes grew back... and fell out... and grew back... and fell out seven times. I quickly realized that eyebrows were more pivotal than the hair. Without them, I didn't have any facial expressions. I felt like an alien without them. Luckily, I had color-matched them at Sephora before they fell out the first time. The beauty consultants taught me how to draw them on naturally. The slicing that I had felt when my hair fell out returned. Apparently, that was what my hair felt like both coming and going. *Slice. Slice. Slice.*

There were days when I'd find myself driving home from work with the radio off. Even in the silence, all I could hear was noise. I craved silence. My senses and perceptions were now hypersensitive.

Sometimes I would be lost in thought about something mundane or trivial and tears would just start streaming down my face. It had been seven months of doing battle in Hell, and I could finally start to think about putting my armor down.

Track 4

'I get by with a little help from my friends'

On January 30, 2012, about seven months since the day I dismissed the bandage under my arm as just a precaution, I rode the elevator up to my last chemotherapy appointment. Friends and family joined Husband and me for the big event.

For months, I had declined all offers from loved ones to attend chemotherapy with us. They were offended, but I knew what awaited them if I took them up on their generosity.

But today, January 30, I watched the horror as it washed over their faces just as it had mine when I first set foot in the infusion room for Chemo 101. I watched their hearts drop as they stepped into the reality that Husband and I had painted into our norm. I saw them realize that while we had made the best of our situation and told the funny side of the story to them for months, there was also a very different side that had gone untold. I watched them try to muster up smiles and feign happiness for this celebration. Just as the carefree spirit in my eyes had died since the photos from the lake so many months ago, I watched the spark in their eyes burn out as they realized this had been anything but fun.

We had spared them from the truth. We had hidden from them the reality of cancer.

Exposing them to this reality dampened my mood a bit,

51

but I still smiled and laughed as they threw confetti and I rang the bell at my last chemo – and quietly hoped I would never have to ring it again. I smiled and laughed with them at lunch and then again when we had a celebratory dinner at my favorite restaurant, the one that had catered our wedding several months earlier. I watched our guests scramble into their cars and drive away as quickly as they could to shut out the reality that was ours. And I still smiled and laughed on the way home.

But when it was all over, I just wanted to crawl in a hole and cry and feel all the things I hadn't let myself feel for so long. It felt like I had driven a Mack truck into a concrete wall and our lives had come to an abrupt halt. We had spent our weekends off together in the infusion room for seven consecutive months. We spent days and weeks staring out the windows at the dismal abyss that was I-35. We knew every gas station and construction zone from Austin to Dallas. For seven months, cancer had been all-consuming.

Now I wasn't sure what I would do with my free time.

The week after chemotherapy ended, I had my surgeon remove my port. It stuck out and was always getting caught on seatbelts and was a visual reminder of what my body had been through. While some thought it was a pacemaker, people who had had cancer could spot it across the room. We'd make eye contact and nod – a special handshake in a secret society. Not a word was spoken, but we knew a lot about the other person when our eyes met and we looked into the window of each other's soul.

I scheduled the appointment to remove the port but forgot to write down any questions. In hindsight, I should have used my powerful skills of deductive reasoning to realize I hadn't been contacted by the hospital about anesthesia. The port sat just below my collarbone and a catheter ran up through my neck and to a large vein by my heart. The doctor intended to snake it out of my neck and work it out of my muscle and scar tissue right then and there – without anesthesia!

Though I had grown numb to the sight of blood, I had never had a catheter removed from my neck. I feared I might faint, so I thought it best to get my special request out of the way: I asked him if I could keep the port when he removed it. While it was an unusual request, he agreed to let me have it once he cleaned it thoroughly and placed it in a biohazard bag.

And with that, he placed numbing cream on my chest and proceeded to slowly run his scalpel across my chest, revealing the quiet companion I had for so long. I couldn't feel any pain, but the pressure of pushing and pulling the port and catheter until they came free at last was concerning. In just a few minutes, the port was out and surgical Super Glue was placed across the opening to suture it closed. I prepared for the itching on the inside to commence; I had always had an allergic reaction to adhesive.

With my port framed and hanging on my closet wall as a daily reminder of the fire we had survived, our lives slipped back into the daily grind of work and chores and our old routine.

*   *   *   *   *

Though chemotherapy was completed, we weren't finished with cancer. There were still surgeries and side effects in the months to come. A month after I completed chemotherapy, the doctor prescribed Tamoxifen to block estrogen and any cancer bandits that somehow may have managed to escape the wrath of the chemo.

A systemic treatment had always been a part of the plan for after chemotherapy. The question had simply been, For how long? Five years? Ten Years? And at what point could I take a break from this treatment to explore carrying my own children?

Tamoxifen perpetuated the hot flashes that I already experienced with the Lupron shots. The estrogen-suppression combined with the chemo brain rendered my memory useless. I wondered if I would go through "the change" again when it was age-appropriate.

No one understood why this seemingly normal young woman was sweating profusely in the winter. The very definition of sex appeal to my new husband, I'd wake in the morning with myself and my sheets drenched in sweat. I was in a tangled mess in the sheets – half-exposed to get some air and half-covered to keep from freezing. Throughout the night, I would put a sleep cap on my head and then take if off. On and off, on and off.

With chemotherapy behind us, everyone wanted to get back to normal. Cancer was gone and in our rearview mirror. This was a constant source of tension and frustration between Husband and me. He wanted to go back to the way things were before cancer. To me, that normal would never exist again. I couldn't imagine ever feeling like the old me again.

Though I fought for it tooth and nail, my carefree spirit was gone. There was still a dullness in my eyes, like someone who had done battle in a war. I'd seen things I couldn't just erase. That feeling wasn't unique to me. Studies show that one in four breast cancer survivors are diagnosed with Post-Traumatic Stress Disorder.

And my physical appearance was forever changed, taking with it my self-confidence. I had suppressed all my estrogen and had the side effects to go with it. My sex drive was mitigated by both physical and mental limitations. I was 31 years old, but I felt like I was 75.

*   *   *   *   *

Everything was somehow bigger and more important after cancer, and not necessarily in a good way. While my priorities were realigned, the importance and pressure I placed on making memories was all-consuming. In my mind, every moment might be my last so it had to be the biggest moment it could be. As cancer chased me in my rear-view mirror, I struggled to have the best anniversary and best birthday and best vacation because they might be my last.

We struggled to see eye to eye. Polly Positive Husband was ready to move on from it all. To him, a birthday or holiday should be just like it was before cancer; to me, it had to be bigger and better. My high expectations left me constantly disappointed, desperately seeking this fictitious perfect memory.

Husband and I managed to escape for a post-chemo celebration with my sister-in-law and brother-in-law. We headed to the races at the Kentucky Derby. For years, I had wanted to go to the Derby. I'm sure this had more to do with my penchant for dressing fancy than anything else, but I also had always been in love with horses. (On more than one occasion in life, I cried at the end of the rodeo when they'd let all the horses run free through the arena.) We rented what was essentially a toy car and drove through Kentucky and Tennessee, following the Bourbon Trail. We laughed so much that it hurt. It was a short trip, but it was the first time in months that we didn't think about cancer. I had a beautiful hat to cover my lack of hair and a fancy dress to cover my scars.

*   *   *   *   *

After we returned from our trip, I was thrust into the world of survivorship. I didn't feel like I belonged. I didn't relate to the term *survivor*. I wanted to wrap my arms around that term like so many others had – even to the point that I made it all the way to the tattoo shop to put it on my arm before I chickened out.

What did *survivor* mean?

Did it mean it was all behind me? Did it mean that it would never come back?

How arrogant was I to think that I could lay claim to that term? It felt like I was daring God to bring it back.

I participated in every breast cancer walk and run and skip and hop. I had photo upon photo made of me hugging my survivor sisters, celebrating our victories. I came, I saw, I got the t-shirt. In fact, I got all the t-shirts. I had more pink crap with pink ribbons on it than I knew what to do with. My jewelry collection was filled with pink plastic crap made in China. I wore it all because I felt that was what I was supposed to do. But deep down in my heart I didn't feel it; I was not a survivor.

I continued to put one foot in front of the other, to play the part of this empowered survivor. Part of me really did feel empowered. But the other part of me sheepishly shrugged my shoulders, hoping I was not tempting fate by celebrating.

Part of moving on was figuring out what birth control to use. In search of a non-hormonal birth control, I approached my OB/GYN. This doctor is the one who diagnosed me with cancer. I felt sure she could help me. This doctor who could hardly look me in the face when she told me I had cancer now seemed bothered by my very presence. Again, she couldn't look me in the eye and was completely dismissive. It took several appointments due to technical difficulties, but with her help I finally got my copper IUD.

When I pressed her with questions about my follow-up schedule for annual exams, she waved it off. She implied that since I couldn't have children, she had little or no interest in me. I stood there with my shoulders shrugged, humiliated and defeated.

I wasn't less of a woman because I was on Tamoxifen, was I? Or was I?

She told me I could have anyone check me every few years. *Anyone? Every few years? How dare she fire me as a patient before I got the chance to fire her as a doctor. Just who in the hell did she think she was?*

Not long after this forgettable appointment, I up and decided I wanted to get a mastectomy on the other side. I wanted to be proactive and do anything I could to make sure I wouldn't wind up in the infusion room again. Whether the second-side mastectomy would prevent that or not was irrelevant. I had no medical degree, but I decided that it would. I woke up one day with the decision made.

Everyone tried to talk me out of it. Everyone said I'd regret it if I didn't have that breast to breastfeed if we had children. Everyone said I'd regret not having part of the old me – an un-marred portion of my body. Everyone told me I wouldn't bond with a baby if I didn't nurse. It wasn't only friends and family with this outpouring of unsolicited advice.

Billboards along I-35 taunted anyone who wouldn't or couldn't breastfeed. They were a constant reminder of the woman I couldn't be. "Babies were meant to be breastfed." *Thanks, Asshole.* What if it's not an option? What if my boobs were in a hazardous waste bin? The signs judged me and made me feel I didn't deserve a child if the milk factory was closed. That was easy for them to say; they didn't live in constant fear that a rogue cancer cell would land them right back in the blue chair. I wanted to give myself the best possible chance of avoiding another round of chemotherapy.

The surgical oncologist was hesitant to do the mastectomy. My age was the issue. I stepped outside while we were out to dinner one night to talk to him after hours. He asked me repeatedly if I was sure as I paced up and down in the parking lot while my food got cold. I was sure. I was annoyed by all these people who wouldn't advise me early on; all of a sudden they stumbled their way into an opinion right about the time I didn't need it nor want it. I had made my decision.

I scheduled my second mastectomy and repeated the process. Everything was the same, only this time I wasn't scared. I knew what to expect. This time it was my choice; I was in control. We repeated the hospital stay, the drugs and the drains. This time I knew to stay ahead of the pain and not refuse the pain medication. This time I knew that I couldn't ever catch up to the pain once it got ahead of me. I went home with two more drains and slid right back into the Heal in Comfort shirt that I had used before. This time we did a slightly better job of tracking the amount of drainage while I pretended to be a good patient. Husband was on guard and wouldn't be sold again on fudging the numbers.

Days passed and I continued to complain that my boob was burning up. (At this stage, when I write "boob," I mean "replacement boob," created with the use of the tissue-expander instrument described in an earlier chapter.)

Husband thought I was crazy, but he didn't turn down the opportunity to do a personal inspection. He swore it was not hot to the touch. The burning sensation drove me crazy. It felt like the inside of my boob was on fire.

One night we were at our friends' house for dinner. The husband in this house is in the helicopter unit of the police department. After years of hearing police-chase stories, I knew this job came with the benefit of heat-sensing goggles. I pulled him aside and asked him if he could get his goggles out of his police car. He was confused, but obliged. Aware that this was not a normal social interaction, I turned to his wife for approval. She nodded in agreement, befuddled at the request, and then I asked him to use his goggles to inspect my boobs and see if one was hotter than the other. After he wiped the tears of laughter from his eyes, he reported that the right one was glowing white, indicating more heat. I was vindicated; my boob was indeed on fire!

The next week, we headed back to Dallas for the drain removal. When the doctor pulled out the drain, I stared down in disbelief as he kept pulling and pulling and pulling. Despite my iron stomach, I felt queasy as I realized how much tubing had been coiled around inside my breast. As he threw the drains into the bio-waste trash can, the throbbing receded and the temperature cooled. Finally, it wasn't hot anymore. And just like that, it was done.

Both my natural breasts were gone.

'I gotta rise up, stand up'

For many reasons, I chose to continue working through-out this experience. It kept me sane and distracted from the dark places in my mind. It kept me in the land of the living instead of the dying.

I sold houses for a living. Yes, I was a garage troll. I was one of "those people" that you had to talk to when you wanted to waste a Saturday looking at model homes.

Working wasn't without some challenges. The combina-tion of chemotherapy, a lack of estrogen and a situation some might deem a little stressful had rendered my brain virtually useless.

I used to have a phenomenal memory. The things in my brain before chemotherapy were 100 percent intact. This meant little jewels - like the lyrics to *Saved by the Bell* or *Fresh Prince of Bel Air*, my very first phone number - were all embed-ded in my mind.

Following chemotherapy, I retained virtually no additional knowledge, and what was retained took constant repetition to remember. Often I would listen to a voicemail at least four times before I was able to write down the return phone num-ber correctly. My brain recognized the numbers, but I'd lose them on the meandering path they took on the way to the pen in my hand. I could hear the number eight, and by the time it got to my hand it was a four.

I had never been good at names, but I could place a face

anywhere. After chemotherapy, I could have a full conversation with someone and leave the room, only to return and greet her as though I'd never met her.

This made it difficult in a high-stress commission sales job in which your ability to earn an income relied on your brain's ability to rattle off answers at lightning speed while anticipating the customer's next question. It also made it hard when the customer wanted to know pricing and details about your product that were ever changing. Even if I could have retained the information, it would change by the next day. Let's not even talk about my ability to recognize clients. This never was an area in which I excelled, but now if you didn't have a funny accent or dress in a weird way I was not going to remember you 20 minutes later.

It was only after my first chemotherapy in 2011 when I realized that with my compromised immune system, one minor sneeze could be a real threat to my health. I could no longer hide my disgust when someone would sneeze into his hand and then reach out to shake mine. I learned to pick up the nearest object to create a diversion when customers walked into my office and to start talking right past the handshake. I would look at clients who knew I was in treatment with a look that said "Really?" when they sat across from me breathing on all my things as they explained that their entire family had the flu. I opened doors with my left hand. I didn't touch my face. I was the girl who wiped down every part of the seat, seatbelt, air vent and tray when I got on an airplane.

My brain was like a black hole. This is a side effect that "regular" people would never understand. When I told others about it, they'd dismiss it as something everyone does, like forgetting why they went into a room. *Oh, that's just because you're distracted; everyone forgets things from time to time.* Let me tell you, it's not the same. It is not even remotely the same. You can't understand it unless you live it.

The sound the heart monitor makes when someone's heart stops beating is what it was like upstairs in my black-hole brain. I didn't just forget. It was like someone got frustrated with the computer and just decided to turn the damn thing off right in the middle of a project.

I once spent five minutes thumbing through my contacts list on my phone to find the name of a friend, a good friend, who would kill me if she knew that despite having known her for years and talking to her on a regular basis, I once spent 15 minutes at a total loss for her name, the first initial of her name, or even an image of what she looked like – until I found it in my phone.

With time, I learned to make the best of it. I'd keep at my fingertips a binder full of information that the customers normally would ask about. Notebooks became key. I had a tough time with paperwork, too. I'd stay late after work for hours, trying with everything I had to make sure my contracts had no mistakes, only to be slapped in the face Monday morning with an e-mail listing all the things I had messed up. It often brought me to tears.

I used to be able to do it all. I used to have some of the best contracts on the sales team. Now it was impossible for me to do a contract without a mistake. Heaven forbid if I finally had to tell someone what was really going on. If so, I had better be prepared for a long drawn-out dialogue about cancer and some dimwitted comment about who they knew who died of cancer.

Even if I got past the question-and-answer session, there was a slew of other issues. I have always been clumsy. Patience wasn't something I was born with, nor was it something I acquired. Add a dose of clumsy to a helping of useless brain, and you might find yourself running over yourself with your car when you forget to throw it in park as you step out to show a client a home. Things weren't firing on all cylinders, and it was hard to coordinate the gas pedal, parking brake and a phenomenal closing technique all at one time. Add five-inch stilettos and a pencil skirt and things weren't pretty.

If the possibility of running over myself with my car wasn't enough, there was the whole wig thing.

A key part of my job is getting people out to home sites, and walking them around and showing them where their dream house might be. Yes, in the five-inch stilettos. If tromping around in heels over rubble and through construction debris – carefully navigating that stream of "water" coming from the port-a-potty – doesn't sound like a great way to spend the afternoon, then add wind and a wig.

I learned years ago that wrap dresses and real estate sales don't mix, but neither do real estate and wigs. While I tried not to kill myself, using one hand for balance, the other hand held onto my wig. I tried to be as discreet as possible, but what I really needed was a chin strap to keep my wig on my head.

Wind also causes static, so if I dared try to straighten my hair to get it out of my face, it would look like I rubbed a balloon on my head. Whenever it was wig time in Cancerland, I learned to carry anti-static dryer sheets in my purse to rub on my hair.

While the wigs offered me a reprieve from looking like I had cancer, the great thing about the wigs at work is that it put my clients and me on a slightly more even playing field. I never knew who they were, and they were fairly confused about whether they knew me as well since I was sporting a different color wig every few days. I took some pleasure in the awkwardness that hung in the air as they tried to study my head during our conversations and figure out if it was my real hair.

Another obstacle I lived with was the loss of feeling in my boobs, post-surgery. My job did require lots of pointing, leaning and demonstrating home features, floor plans and home sites. Any of the above could cause a wardrobe malfunction and unfortunately, with no nerve endings, I would never know. So, I walked into my sales partner's office and sat down to ask him a favor. He and I were great friends and had too much fun working together for it to be called work. I asked him if he would promise to do something counterintuitive to male nature: tell me if my boob was ever out since I had no idea if I was going to flash someone at any moment. He graciously agreed.

Track 6

'Have you ever seen the rain?'

M onths passed and life moved on. I had continuous pain
in my abdomen. Naturally, I thought it was cancer, but
"insurance standard of care" reared its ugly head again.

"No scan," was the verdict.

A visit to a drive-by doctor sent me to my new OB/GYN;
she ordered an ultrasound. Though it wasn't a known side
effect of my anti-estrogen drug, quite a few of my friends and
I were suffering from ovarian cysts. My doctor scheduled me
for an ultrasound and bloodwork to test for ovarian cancer
every six weeks.

I begged my oncologist to remove my ovaries. It seemed so
futile to have to deal with this nuisance when our kids were
on ice. She said I was too young. When I didn't make headway with her, I appealed to my gynecologist and begged her to
remove my ovaries. As much as I loved her, I really didn't need
to see her every month and a half. I was met with the same
answer: too young.

Both doctors felt that I would regret this decision. Apparently, I was too young to make these decisions for myself, but I
wasn't too young to go through the life-altering experiences of
cancer and chemotherapy and a mastectomy, twice. Addition-
ally, it wasn't considered "medically necessary," so insurance
would not cover this elective surgery. All I wanted was to add
my ovaries – these "problem children" – to a biohazard bucket
with my boobs and any other useless organ that could just

cause problems. I started eyeing my appendix and wondered if I could get a bulk discount.

I had a dream one night that rattled me to my very core. The details were blurry, but the message was clear. When Husband woke up, I told him I didn't want to carry a child. I told him we would need a gestational carrier for the embryos. I knew in my heart that I couldn't take the risk to carry my own child. Husband was taken aback and confused. There he was, rattling around in his normal everyday life. He thought things would go back to the way they were before cancer. He assumed I would carry a child once I was off Tamoxifen. We'd have a child just like everyone else.

In his defense, there was no warning shot fired. I sprang this decision on him just like when I shaved off my hair out of the blue and decided to do an elective mastectomy on the non-cancer side. While I sat quietly during the car rides to Dallas, my brain carefully weighed the pros and cons of each decision. Since he hadn't been involved in the discussions in my head, these decisions seemingly came out of nowhere.

Just like with the elective mastectomy, every fiber of my being knew that I shouldn't try to carry our child. When Husband didn't make any headway with me, he spoke to friends and coworkers. The people who had been so mum when I desperately needed them were once again full of opinions. Everyone told him it was a bad decision and that I wouldn't bond with my child. And besides that, it would cost a fortune to have a gestational carrier. Apparently, an oven wasn't cheap. Insurance would not cover the birth, the exams or ultrasounds.

I could see his brain working fervently, calculating the financial impact of this decision down to the nearest decimal. He was deliberate and analytical. I was not. To Husband, the sheer opportunity to analyze a decision offered him some semblance of control in this otherwise chaotic situation.

Though outside influences chipped away at my armor, I held my ground. Whenever I started to doubt my decision, I'd get a swift kick in the gut. The message was clear. I didn't see how my love for or my relationship with my child would be any different than that of an adoptive parent.

After nine months of ultrasounds every six weeks, the ovarian pain finally got to be too much. I had developed a hemorrhagic cyst, which caused additional swelling in my abdomen. We scheduled surgery to remove the cysts. This would be my eleventh surgery since my cancer diagnosis. After months of insomnia, I looked forward to the anesthesia-induced sleep.

The surgeons made three incisions in my abdomen to remove the cysts, including one in my belly button. The CO_2 they injected to enlarge my abdomen during the surgery slowly crept from my belly into my chest and shoulders over the next few weeks and caused horrific pain.

Though I suffered from physical pain as a result of that surgery, the unrelated mental and emotional pain I was dealing with was taking a greater toll. Days and weeks went by and I continued to wake each morning in a cold sweat. I tried to reason myself out of my paranoia: I felt well; I was taking care of myself; I had finally adjusted to the hot flashes and hormonal swings of medically induced menopause. In spite of all of that, I was increasingly irritable. Something was wrong.

Even my dog sensed it. This was about the same time my loyal German Shepherd, Heidi, started avoiding me. She and I had a unique relationship. She was my sidekick in life and was never more than a few inches from my side. Any dog-friendly place I went, Heidi was with me. I had had her since she was a few weeks old. On numerous occasions, she had put herself between me and someone she felt was a threat. Now, all of a sudden, she was nowhere to be found. I remarked to Husband how odd it was. She wasn't at my feet, or under foot, and wouldn't even let me feed her.

Over the past year, my intuition had earned some credibility with Husband. My intuition had a pretty good track record to date. I scheduled an appointment with my nurse practitioner to talk about my concerns and to demand a scan. I felt her eyes watching me as I explained my concerns. I could feel the word "hypochondriac" itching to roll off the tip of her tongue. She wrote me a prescription for anti-depressants.

So, I really had nothing to justify this scan other than a feeling deep in my gut. I felt great. I was healthy and exercised regularly. I had a high-pressure, full-time job. The nurse practitioner tried to assure me that I was fine:

"You're young. You're healthy. You look great."

We talked at length about anxiety. I could tell she felt my fears were unfounded. She told me insurance likely wouldn't cover the cost of the scan and encouraged Husband and me to re-think the scan, due to the cost. Nothing she said would change my mind. In that moment, cost was irrelevant. It was a gamble we were willing to take. We offered to write her a check on the spot. While she felt my fears were irrational, she sensed the desperation in my voice and finally, finally she ordered the scan.

She was able to work me in for an appointment the next morning. I showed up and repeated my barium protocol. (As they started the IV, I thought about how I had not missed the taste of burnt skunk.) I shivered through the scan – a combination of temperature and nerves. Once the scan was over, I felt a deep sense of relief. Whether or not my anxiety was founded, at least I would know for sure whether the cancer was back. The unknown was all-consuming. Having laid the burden of my future at the radiologist's feet, Husband and I went to the gym to burn off some nervous energy.

* * * * *

Three missed calls.

When we returned to the car after our workout, "3 Missed Calls" burned bright on my cell phone's screen. Three missed calls from my oncologist in tight succession. Well, shit. Nearly two years of cancer taught me good news never came quickly. Good news only came after days of waiting. This was too soon.

Seconds ticked by as I stared at my phone before I finally gathered the nerve to return the call. It seemed like a long time passed before the doctor's office finally answered. As soon as I told the receptionist my name, the nurse practitioner who ordered the scan grabbed the phone out of her hand.

Her voice trembled as she told me it was cancer.

Then her voice cracked when she told me the cancer had spread to my liver.

Maybe it was guilt – knowing she had discouraged me from getting a scan. Maybe it was the shock of realizing a patient's outward appearance had little bearing on what was happening inside her body. Maybe it was the realization that it could have been her.

I was 33 and only two days older than she. We had become friends outside the world of cancer. We had the same taste in wine. She and my oncologist had constantly remarked that I was the healthiest person with cancer they knew. If this could happen to me, it could happen to anyone. Through the tremors, she asked us to come into the office immediately. It was *déjà vu.*

The only difference between this time and last time was that the reason for my visit wasn't a mystery. There was no need to agonize over what the results might be. It had been just 22 months since my initial cancer diagnosis.

I looked across the console of the truck and locked eyes with Husband as I hung up the phone.

"Well, shit," I said.

There was no time for emotion. We fell lock-step back into

the precision of the routine we had practiced so many times before. We each had our roles and we knew what had to be done. We were still in the parking lot as we sprang into action on the way to this oncology party where the dress code was "come as you are." I texted several of my metastatic breast cancer friends as Husband began the obligatory calls to family and friends. He was the Chief Communications Officer. I was the Director of Planning and Research.

Metastatic cancer meant cancer had spread beyond the original location to other organs. I didn't know much about metastatic cancer. All I knew was that metastatic cancer was Stage 4 cancer and that there was no Stage 5. In the 20 minutes it took to get to the doctor, my friends gave me a list of questions to ask.

Where was the cancer?

How much had it grown?

Would we test to see if it was hormone-positive?

Would I do chemotherapy or radiation?

Was surgery an option?

Would I still be estrogen-positive?

From the doctor's vantage point, I'm sure the visit went better than she anticipated. She had prepared with Kleenex and hugs, but my metastatic phone-a-friends had helped me fast-forward through emotions, quickly skipping over panic and grief. I was an emotional vault; I was on lockdown. I didn't shed a tear as she delivered the news. I was the calm before the storm. I was stoic, knowing that while I wished the news was different, I never doubted the outcome when I was demanding the scan.

Though I was asymptomatic, all the medical degrees in the world didn't matter. I knew my own body and I knew something was wrong. I never felt comfortable in the "survivor" shoes. It was like my body had known all along.

The doctor reviewed the scan with us and said we had

caught it early. There were just a few small lesions in my liver, the largest of which was 2.3 centimeters, the exact same measurement of the original tumor in my breast. The cancer made up only about two percent of my liver. There was also a questionable lymph node, but she was not concerned with it as we would treat the cancer systemically. Systemic treatment meant that the medicine would go throughout my entire body, not just to one organ.

We began to formulate a plan. The next step was a liver biopsy, to determine if this was the same type of cancer, followed by extensive genetic testing, which would take weeks. We would need to make a decision on treatment before we received those findings – because time was of the essence.

As we started to leave, I turned back to my oncologist and looked her squarely in the eyes without blinking. My words were both calm and deliberate:

"I don't ever want to hear the phrase 'insurance standard of care' in regards to my treatment again."

And with that, it was done.

The doctor had done nothing wrong. She had followed protocol, but never again would I be a slave to insurance. We would decide how much money my life was worth, not any doctor or insurance company. I was truly blessed to have a great job with phenomenal insurance, but if I had left my health up to the insurance company, I never even would have had a mammogram. If left to the "insurance standard of care," I would be dead.

As we headed down the hall, the nurse handed me a prescription for Xanax with sadness in her eyes, anticipating that at some point I would start to process real emotions associated with this recurrence. I took one the second I picked it up from the pharmacy. The Xanax only compounded the calm, as I nonchalantly called family and friends to deliver the news. My tone had little more excitement than reporting that we were out of milk.

Just a few days later, I attended an event remembering the sisters we had lost that year to metastatic cancer. My own bad news had spread like wild fire through the breast cancer community. Ironically, I was seen as the healthiest cancer patient they knew.

I had planned to attend this event previously, to honor those we lost. I didn't know I would also be scoping out where I wanted my candle to be on the table when I followed in their footsteps. A friend who had been surrounded by these women for a long time handed me a book by David Kessler, *Visions, Trips and Crowded Rooms: Who and What You See Before You Die.* She had great intentions, but was not aware that my shock had not yet worn off. I was nowhere near acceptance of the idea that my days were numbered. I had fast-forwarded through all those emotions into action and was ill-prepared to start the prep course for my death. Three days prior I was fine. Now I needed to read a book about how to deal with dying?

Timing, people. Timing is everything. Timing and filters, more specifically.

* * * * *

Prepared for battle, we marched into another surgery, right through visions, trips and crowded rooms. A liver biopsy would determine if I had liver cancer or breast cancer in my liver. Though subtle in wording, the distinction was of grave importance. It was difficult to process which camp I wanted to fall into.

Breast cancer in my liver would mean that I had Stage 4 metastatic breast cancer. When cancer spreads to other parts of the body, it is called metastatic cancer. Even though it is in a new location – for me, my liver – it is still named after the area where it started.

Metastatic cancer would mean that some rogue cells had escaped the massacre from surgeries, the nuclear explosions of chemotherapy, the fly-overs of a daily oral medication to block estrogen, and the watchful eye of scan surveillance – and somehow made it out alive. Little bastards!

I didn't know which side I was supposed to be cheering for. Did I want metastatic breast cancer or did I want liver cancer? (Candidly, I wanted a cabana boy on the beach bringing me bottomless mimosas, but no one got that memo.) If I had breast cancer in my liver, I would not qualify for a liver transplant because I didn't have liver cancer. The transplant list was for people with liver cancer, not simply people with cancer in their liver. It was a small, but inconvenient loophole in the system.

As I lay shivering in the Arctic room, they overlaid my scans over my body. This was a high-tech version of a high school overhead projector and a transparency. Instead of cutting me wide open, they would use the scans as a guide to find the lesions. I sure hoped I didn't sneeze.

Before I drifted off to sleep during the CT guided biopsy, they showed me the largest lesion. They would take several core samples that we could use for current genetic testing and future diagnostics.

The biopsy itself went swimmingly from my vantage point under anesthesia, but I awoke in a horrendous amount of pain. I couldn't even think about my liver because the pain in my arm caused me to continually seize forward every time the blood pressure cuff filled with air. I locked eyes with my mom, and I saw her eyes well up with tears. She thought I was having a heart attack and had to turn and look away. Every time the blood pressure cuff filled, I would lunge forward in excruciating pain. My family scrambled to find a nurse or the doctor, but everyone had vanished.

The nurses couldn't do anything to alleviate the pain.

Eventually, the doctor appeared, but he could not offer any solutions. I asked him to remove the blood pressure cuff and he said he didn't have that authority. Who would have the authority to remove the cuff if not a doctor? Time was standing still. The pain was debilitating and everyone was frozen in red tape. I finally ripped the cuff off on my own, setting off all the bells and whistles and alarms on the machine. That was one way to get some damn attention in that joint!

After I removed the cuff, I stopped seizing to an upright position and could finally relax enough to feel the pain from the biopsy. Apparently, the cuff had put too much pressure on the nerves in my arm. Apparently, that happens in only two percent of patients. Apparently, there was no one at this hospital with any authority to remove the cuff other than myself. I don't know if I even had the authority. I guessed I would find out when I got the bill.

* * * * *

Once released from the hospital, we added more wear and tear to what I affectionately called "the cancer car." The car shuttled us across the state in search of the right doctor. This time we really were shopping for a doctor to save my life. Convenience was irrelevant. We would drive or fly to whoever gave me the best chance at life.

Though I had been in the cancer world for a few years now, it was only then that I truly understood I couldn't have died from early-stage breast cancer. People died only after the cancer spread and started shutting down organs. That would have been great information to have had much earlier on this journey.

There was a certain peace that came with knowing this. While I'd love to have found myself in any pair of shoes but my own, there was also a calm that came with not having to wonder anymore, not having to look back over my shoulder. No one and nothing was chasing me anymore. There was no more agonizing about whether it would come back. It was back, sitting right next to me.

We drove back and forth across the state and faxed records to doctors across the country. We tried to get in to see the best of the best, but were often lost in the bureaucracy of the medical field. We either needed a referral to see the best or we pulled a ticket and would see the next available doctor in line. I called for weeks to get into one major facility, without a single returned phone call. When I finally reached them, they scheduled me with a doctor who had horrible reviews online. It was him or no one.

The pressure to make the right next step was overwhelming. Each doctor offered a different plan. Would I need to pull my port out of retirement for chemotherapy, or would I try hormonal treatment? I found myself praying for doors to open where they needed to open and close where they needed to close. I finally made peace with the idea that the silence on the other end of the phone was an answered prayer for a closed door.

* * * * *

With miles of highway in front of us, my thoughts wandered as I stared out the window. I replayed the elephant in the room over and over again in my head. I had been told that I had 24 to 36 months to live. This shit show had started a few weeks before I was 31. I was now 33. If I was lucky, they thought I'd live to see 36.

Where had I gone wrong? I re-evaluated the decisions I had made so many months before.

Was that original oncologist right?

Did we not remove enough lymph nodes?

Should I have done radiation after all?

And, what if the troll was right? Maybe I should have been more concerned with whether I would live or die rather than my prospects of having children.

The biopsy came back positive for metastatic breast cancer. We learned that the cancer was being fed by estrogen more than before. I didn't know how my body was somehow making more food for this son-of-a-bitch in spite of the Lupron shots and the systemic treatments. The doctors' shoulders slumped when they realized I did not have the Her2 protein again. While the Her2 characteristics meant more available treatments, it also meant my cancer had mutated from my original diagnosis, and we were now fighting a whole new battle. I rolled my eyes at their visible defeat.

Our feet found familiar paths as we met with the doctor at UT Southwestern, a doctor I had met with years before. Her nurse gave me a Lupron shot to begin to shut down my ovaries while we waited for an oophorectomy, to remove my ovaries and fallopian tubes. There was only one doctor she'd allow to do the oophorectomy - you know, back to this best of the best grading scale. Every doctor I had consulted agreed that removing my ovaries would reduce the estrogen feeding my cancer. After months of doctors telling me that an oophorectomy was not medically necessary, suddenly it was at the forefront of their minds - the obvious next step.

After months of insurance dictating that I didn't need any scans, I found myself back in countless tubes, thinking how much cheaper it would have been for my insurance company to have allowed the scans before the cancer recurred. During the scans, I struggled to hold my breath and breathe on demand, having just had a needle stuck deep into my liver. I felt I might suffocate in the tube as the pressure built inside my lungs.

As I moved from tube to tube, the germaphobe in me

kicked in. I wasn't a germaphobe before I got cancer. Cancer had turned me into one. Living with a compromised immune system brought with it an extreme awareness of my surroundings. I amused my husband when I wiped down everything in an airplane and never touched anything with my bare hands. I'd hold my drink in my lap, avoiding the tray tables. (Of course, that was only amplified by the time I rode next to a woman that sucked her fake fingernails off and spit them on the tray.) When I'd meet people, I was increasingly aware that I had just seen them sneeze in their right hand before they reached out to shake mine.

I lay there staring at the plastic tubing inches from my face, wondering if anyone ever cleaned the inside of this thing. What if someone sneezed? How many people sneezed in this thing over the years? There were few things in life I hated more than a sneeze. Sneezes and those creepy clear geckos. I wasn't claustrophobic, but the thought of all the creepy crawly germs that might be in this tube with me was starting to make my skin crawl. It was my own personal version of *Fear Factor*.

While the doctor agreed that we would utilize systemic treatment, she did want to confirm whether the lymph node was positive for cancer. Fortunately, in such a large facility, we were able to go upstairs and have the biopsy done immediately. The nurses were amazing, with the exception of one. While she helped the other nurse prep for the biopsy, this one labored on and on about what she would do if she ever found out she had cancer. As I lay immobilized on the table, trapped and unable to escape, she rambled on about if she would even consider modern medicine. The irony was not lost on me.

* * * * *

We traveled back and forth between Austin and Dallas for scans and consultations, weighing all of our treatment options. Friends and family provided a welcome distraction during these visits.

At dinner one evening, I felt like a bystander in my own life. I was lost in thought as I looked down at my salad, pushing the lettuce around the plate with my fork. I studied it and thought of all the salads I had eaten over the course of my life. My diet in large part consisted of salad, fruits and vegetables. I had eaten an apple a day my entire life. Clearly, the old adage was complete and total bullshit. An apple a day did not keep the doctor away. All the apples in the world had led me straight to Stage 4 cancer.

I lifted my head and looked across the restaurant, surveying the fare at the other tables: cheese and fried foods and calories galore. I stared as they washed down their food with beer before going outside to smoke a cigarette. I looked back down at my salad for what seemed like an eternity. I felt tears well up in the corner of my eyes, once again quietly humming, "One of these things is not like the other one" and wondering, *How in the hell did I get here?*

Days later, the doctor confirmed the lymph node was positive for breast cancer. The questions came flooding in. Did the original surgeon miss this lymph node? Did it somehow hide from chemotherapy?

I wanted someone to blame, but did it really matter? What did all the blame in the world really accomplish? The cancer was back. All the finger pointing wouldn't make it go away. I didn't have the time or the energy to waste to find the culprit. I had to start kicking and screaming again in the fight for my life.

I somehow had to finish a crash course in coping with dying so I could focus on living.

'So tired, tired of waiting'

As I waited for my appointment with the gynecological oncologist to discuss the oophorectomy, the Lupron shots threw me right back into a state in which I was sweating or freezing or sweating and freezing at the same time.

I weathered the fall in shorts and leg warmers, unsure what my internal temperature would be from minute to minute. I had blankets and cooling pillows across the bed. Husband was going to have to fend for himself. I was just trying to survive a heat wave followed by a blizzard, entering menopause for the second time at just 33 years of age.

In October of 2013, I underwent my cystectomy. Three incisions were made in my abdomen to remove the cysts from my ovaries likely caused by my cancer-prevention medication. A month later, three additional incisions were made, one inch above their predecessors, so the ovaries could be removed. This was after a week of being shuttled between doctors in Dallas consulting on treatment options; they all agreed that removing my ovaries was the best thing to do to fight my cancer. The cancer was fed primarily by estrogen, so removing the largest producers of estrogen seemed to be a no-brainer.

While under anesthesia, the doctor removed my IUD and biopsied my uterus for cancer. After all, I had been taking a drug to prevent a breast cancer recurrence that, as a side effect, could cause uterine cancer. I was finally cleared for surgery when I passed my fourth urine test of the week; this test was to ensure I wasn't pregnant. They were nothing if not thorough.

When we arrived for surgery, they handed me a yellow tartan plaid ensemble. The yellow indicated I was a fall risk. The plaid indicated someone had incredibly poor taste or a phenomenal sense of humor. The ensemble handicapped my sales pitch and made me look like a crazed woman as I tried to persuade the doctor why this should be an outpatient surgery. We had been living out of a suitcase for days. Actually, when I look back on it, we had been living out of a suitcase on and off since June of 2011. I wanted out of the car and I wanted to be in my own bed.

I lost the battle with the doctor, but I was victorious in anesthesia. Before I passed out, we agreed that if I was up and walking, I could go home after a night's stay in the hospital. The next day I changed out of my fall-risk yellows and into my baby blues so that I was free to roam around the hospital without calling attention to myself. I ran into my doctor in the hall while I was doing laps, and she just shook her head, "Young people." She agreed to let me go if I agreed not to return to work for three weeks. I obliged long enough to sign the release forms and then promptly returned to work two days later.

I surely didn't need the HR troll chasing me down about appropriate and inappropriate leaves of absence! I imagined telling her, *You stay in your golden office, and I'll stay here and work from a fetal position. That way, everyone wins.*

A few days later, as I folded myself into my car seat to drive to work, I had some serious second thoughts as the pain and nausea nearly overwhelmed me. But there was no turning back now. I knew myself and I knew I'd curl up in a ball at my desk long before I would admit defeat.

* * * * *

True to form, the genetic testing results from my liver biopsy came back on a Friday at 5 p.m. over Thanksgiving weekend. I had quickly grown to hate holidays. Holidays were just code words for everyone shuts down three days earlier and so any life-changing information you might want is on hold until they get back in and settled, probably closer to later the next week. Everyone who was anyone was gone and we were left in total suspension, making no forward progress in our fight.

The oncologist recommended a two-drug combination as the best next step. Our good buddy, "Insurance Standard of Care," had other plans. Insurance Standard of Care dictated that I follow another course of treatment. I needed to follow this other treatment for six weeks and fail it before I could proceed with the doctor's recommendation.

Hold on! That doesn't work for me. I'm not sure who it does work for. Maybe it worked for people who were not as vocal and hard-headed as I was.

I wasn't the smartest person in the world, but I was logical. The people on the other end of the phone weren't doctors. Their logic was flawed at best. No, it was just plain dumb. The more treatments I failed, the more expensive I would become to my insurance carrier. We had caught my cancer relatively early. It was small. It was manageable.

What would happen in six weeks on potentially the wrong drug? How out of control could this get?

I dug in my heels and proceeded to spend the rest of my Thanksgiving holiday in the back bedroom of my parents' home – which was in Arkansas at the time – playing telephone tag with the skeleton crew insurance team, working on an appeal. To add insult to injury, I was stuck on a Jack-in-the-Box connection, with static streaming constantly through the phone as I yelled desperately over the crackling to the voice on the other end of the line. Cell phone reception was spotty at best. I couldn't risk hanging up the phone and starting over.

Over and over for hours on end, I re-explained my situation to whatever poor soul answered the phone. I tried to be patient and nice, knowing it was no one's fault I was in this predicament, but with each explanation I became more exasperated than with the last. Husband tried to tag me out, but I was the star of this show and the only one who could answer the insurance company's questions.

In the end, I threw up my hands. I told them to have the drugs ready for me when I arrived in Dallas Monday, then I hung up the phone to salvage what was left of the holiday. We would work out the payment somehow, some way. What wasn't going to happen was for me to get on a drug the doctor already knew would fail.

While we sat in the waiting room Monday morning, my phone rang. I recognized the number immediately. After all, I had dialed and re-dialed it countless times over Thanksgiving weekend. The insurance company had approved my appeal. Apparently, if anyone was willing to go to as much trouble as I had over a holiday weekend, well, that was all you needed. And, just like that, I became the squeaky wheel that got the attention. Working in customer service, where the customers are always right even when they are very, very wrong, I despised rewarding bad behavior. However, it looked like being the loudest was the only way I was going to be heard. This was my life we were talking about. No one was going to fight for my life as hard as I would.

I was going to go down squeaking. No amount of WD-40 would fix this squeak as I fought for my life.

* * * * *

Exploring all options meant sticking a toe into the crunchy granola society that is Austin, Texas. The city motto is "Keep Austin Weird." I defied everything that this saying stood for –

hemp necklaces, hiking shoes as appropriate footwear for all occasions, and all things crunchy and granola.

But I must admit that in the fight for my life, I dabbled in holistic and Chinese medicine, organic foods, meditation and any crackpot idea friends and family found on the Internet. I took a spoonful of baking soda and maple syrup every day. I ate asparagus by the carload.

I tried oils and juicing and any other suggestion they had: broth from boiled cow's feet (which is disgusting, by the way), acupuncture, apple cider vinegar. In my head, I would roll my eyes, but desperate times called for desperate measures. There was no shortage of Facebook posts or how-to-beat-cancer e-mails forwarded to me to keep me occupied.

I was disappointed that the "biggest bullet in my gun" – the removal of my ovaries – didn't result in lower tumor markers for weeks to come. Patience wasn't a trait I was born with, nor was it anything I had acquired over the previous 33 years. If anything, I had headed in the opposite direction.

On one hand, cancer made me more tolerant of stupid commentary and more understanding of everyday struggles. It made me take a deep breath and just patiently wait as the woman in front of me scanned coupon after coupon after coupon at the checkout line. In the very same breath, cancer made me more exasperated with how much I still had to do in so little time. I had a bomb strapped to my chest, or, more specifically, to my liver. I would get road rage in the grocery store. *Get out of my way!*

I was at a standstill with patience. The doctor reiterated it might take a while for the ovary removal to take effect and for the drugs to make an impact on my numbers. I wanted instant gratification. I expected my estrogen levels to plummet right away.

True to form, we dealt with the stress by boarding a cruise out of Galveston. This was my worst nightmare, only compounded by our recent visit to the Titanic Museum in Branson, Missouri. Planning on boarding a large boat? Then by all means, go see an exact replica of a large boat that sank after departure.

Despite the shit show I had been fully immersed in for the past few years, drowning was my worst nightmare, so naturally we boarded the "Coffin on the Sea." We combined my visceral fear of drowning at sea with an extreme case of germaphobia. Clearly, the only way to navigate this ship was to tuck my hands into my sleeves and use my sleeves to touch any railings and doorways.

* * * * *

Everything was tangled up in red tape. Every form and survey and questionnaire had the loaded checkbox: "Have you ever had cancer?" I began to wonder what the repercussions would be for lying on these forms. If I was doing something my oncologist approved of, did I have to disclose this information to this third party? Were there some sort of Cancer Police roaming around?

I have an earache.

Well, it says here you have cancer.

Yea, that's irrelevant. I just have an earache – you know, like a normal person!

Yea, I'm probably going to need to send you back to your oncologist for a brain scan.

Things were no different out on the open waters of the Gulf of Mexico. Husband and I attempted to relax with a couple's massage, but instead ended up paying for the masseuse to tell me that my back pain was not a result of the hemorrhaged liver biopsy, but a clear sign that the cancer had spread from my liver to my kidneys.

I was certain she wasn't going to get a tip for making me cry through my massage.

Thanks for the useless piece of information with no supporting evidence!

I left this hour of relaxation with tears running down my face, desperate to make an Internet connection to reach my oncologist. Did I have kidney cancer now? Or breast cancer in my kidneys? Did this Jamaican masseuse know something I didn't know? I was out to sea with no access to the Internet to quell my fears. I shirked away to our cubby hole to curl up in bed and cry and attempt to find some sort of warmth inside this Arctic ship. We were on a cruise in December because we were trying to get *warm*.

* * * * *

Week after week, I took the two-drug combo that I had fought so hard to receive. It was great to get medication without having to be back in the blue chair, but the waiting was debilitating. How did we know if it was working? At least when my hair fell out, we had some indication that surely it was working on something, right? The numbers continued to creep up and the scan showed progression of the disease, but we soldiered on. Tumors could die from the inside out and the necrosis would cause swelling which would throw the liver enzymes out of whack. We were in a high-stakes game of "wait and see."

I didn't excel at being idle at anything. I couldn't even try to take a nap without seeing something that needed to be organized or rearranged.

After a few weeks, my dog Heidi came back around and was my fur-buddy again, at my side everywhere I went. They say dogs can smell cancer. I wondered if Heidi had known something was wrong. I was a little peeved that my trusted canine would feel that the best way to deal with my recurrence was to abandon ship. But she was quickly forgiven, of course.

After Super Bowl Sunday, we braved the Texas Icepocolypse and headed to Dallas. In Texas, the roads are shut down at the slightest hint of ice. We were scheduled for back to back appointments in Dallas on Monday, and no amount of condensation was going to get between me and the answers to my questions. If we could make it from Austin to Dallas, the doctors damn well could make it from their homes to the hospital to quell my rapidly growing insanity. I needed to know once and for all if my cancer was responding to this treatment.

* * * * *

Very soon after our arrival at the doctor's office, I started to notice the looks in the waiting room. It didn't matter their ages. One after another, I'd get these looks of disdain from the other patients and their families.

They'd look me up and down from head to toe. At the time, I still had my hair and I was well-accessorized. I rolled up to every appointment in my 5-inch heels with a smile on my face. I was a big believer in faking it until you made it. I felt better when I looked better. I was hard-pressed to see why I should have to look sick in order to get accepted into this Rush Week of a waiting room. Apparently, I didn't look sick enough to be inducted into the club. I looked back at them with thoughts running through my head, knowing that in all likelihood my Stage 4 cancer diagnosis was far worse than theirs.

These looks didn't wane when my hair fell out and I wore wigs. They didn't wane when my hair started growing back. Because I did my best to not look sick, I wasn't invited into the Cool Kid's Club. I just received hateful stares from all the patrons at the doctor's office.

Cancer isn't one size fits all. I didn't expect anyone to dress up or wear a wig who didn't want to, but I wasn't going to throw away my identity just because it made them feel better for me to commiserate alongside them. That's the difference with Stage 4 cancer. Sometimes treatments leave you with hair and minimal side effects that allow you to feel somewhat normal; sometimes treatments knock you on your ass. The only part I had to play was me – getting up and fighting and being the best me I knew how, even if I didn't fit into the cliques in the waiting room.

Get up. Dress up. Show up. Never give up. This motto didn't always come easily. It wasn't without difficulty. I didn't always feel like getting dressed up, but I made it a point to do so. As long as I could dress up, I was going to dress up. Every day was a smoky eye makeup day because that was the only way to conceal the eyelashes that came and left as quickly as the wind. And, due to simple rote memory, my feet were much more coordinated in high heels than they were in flat shoes. Wearing heels logistically ensured that I would stay upright – if only I could avoid running over myself with my car.

* * * * *

Hospitals, doctors and nurses everywhere – may I have your attention, please.

Listen up as I describe what it's like to live in the mind of someone with cancer. Let's just tell it like it is. We're nuts! End of story. What did you expect? You told me to notify you of every ache and pain, but if I notified you of too many aches and pains, I was a hypochondriac. In our minds, there is no possible way that any ache or pain is anything other than a cancer recurrence.

Hang nail? – Cancer.

Eyelash stuck in your eye? – Cancer.

Muscle Pain? – Cancer.

Headache? – Oh... that one is *definitely* cancer.

You take someone who is certifiable and you play your game of musical waiting room chairs.

First, you made me get there an hour early before my scans to drink this wonderful barium-laced milkshake – which is really no better for my body than adding water to cocaine and calling it a day. I was somewhat curious what would happen if my company did a random drug test after I drank this stuff. I can hear it now:

"You test positive for...yea, we don't even know what that is. You're radioactive for sure."

For anyone unfortunate enough to be duped into drinking this milkshake, I have some advice: Pick the banana flavor. Do not pick the "mixed berry." And whatever you do, don't pick the "mocha." Don't take their damn straw. Chug it. Chug it like you learned how in college – and be done with it.

Fortunately, I was able to drink this shake in the company of friends and family, there for moral support and distraction. Occasionally, Husband would provide a lovely musical medley in the form of his snoring in the waiting room for all to enjoy.

After an hour, the nurses provided some sort of hope that our waiting would soon end as they called me to come to the back.

Unfortunately, they weren't really calling me back. They were only calling me back to this little private waiting room that is about 15 steps closer for the techs. That's for when they decided it was finally time to put me out of my misery. They took me away from my friends and family and people-watching, only to sit by my lonesome in a smaller, less comfortable waiting room, with a TV that was stuck on an annoying show at a ridiculously high volume, without a remote control, for at least another 30 minutes. As I searched desperately for something to throw through this TV, I was called back officially for my scan. Time for my IV, the skunk-tasting saline flush, then the contrast dye.

"Inhale."

"Hold your breath."

"Release."

This bossy robot living inside the CT machine and I were practically on a first-name basis. I wish I could change his accent like I did Siri's. British Siri and I got along much better than American Siri and I. American Siri is really snarky when she disapprovingly shakes her head, "Recalculating."

The scan took about five minutes – ten, if you count the time it took to stab my vein and twist it in a circle until it was straight. *That didn't hurt at all.* I'm not sure if they knew this, but I do have more than one vein in my arm. Husband thought the scan took 45 minutes. Some of them did, but this one did not. He had no idea I was just climbing the walls of my padded cell for most of that time.

We usually had to wait for hours between my scans and the actual doctor's appointments. So, rather than sitting around and twiddling our thumbs, sometimes we left the building and saddled up to a bar, or threw money away at the mall in between appointments. We would make it back to the hospital in time for our appointments to be shuffled between another set of waiting rooms. We sat in one sitting room for bloodwork and moved to another, smaller room for more waiting.

And we sat.

And we waited.

Hours of our lives were wasted in waiting rooms, where other patients looked on with disdain at my audacity to sit alongside them, "pretending to be sick." We spent a ton of time being shuttled between appointments and waiting rooms and filling out the same damn forms I'd filled out the week before.

Isn't this already in your computer?

Eventually, they'd call us back under the guise of progress – to get my blood pressure and weight – before our final resting space in the enclosed patient room with no windows and no way to get out. I couldn't imagine why my blood pressure was off the charts.

I understood. More and more people were getting cancer. "Hide yo' kids. Hide yo' wife and Hide yo' husband." I apologize. That was an unfortunate reference to Antoine Dobson, well worthy of the YouTube search. (I'll pause for your viewing entertainment.)

You're welcome.

Anyway, they are getting busier and it's taking more time to get results.

But for every minute that passed, I convinced myself that I hadn't seen the doctor because the results were so bad that she was desperately calling the best experts around the world to figure out what to do. We waited long enough that I needed to use the bathroom. So, I walked right by the doctor in her office. She was on the phone, clearly making these desperate calls regarding my scan results. (In reality, she just may have been ordering lunch.)

If that wasn't enough, I had to strut myself down the hall to the restroom in this "cape." This "cape," as they affectionately call it, was clearly designed by a man who was into *Xena: Warrior Princess*. No woman would have designed this. First, it wasn't a cape. It was a half-cape. I looked like a super hero with a loin cloth for a cape. It covered only half my torso and conveniently featured two snaps. The two snaps happen to be located in such a way that I might as well not even use them because my boobs were hanging out either way. I hurried to the bathroom with my head hanging down, desperately grasping at the fabric to cover myself.

When the doctor finally arrived, we were numb from our long day of being shuttled between waiting rooms. This was a teaching hospital, so she had a resident – a resident who was thoroughly distracted by my boobs.

The doctor continued with niceties and cordial conversations. I was having a hard time focusing on her words as she explained that some of the tumors appeared to be shrinking. I was incredibly distracted by this resident who was obviously seeing a boob for the first time. He couldn't make eye contact with me and was starting to develop a facial twitch. Since my boobs had become merely appendages to me after years of inspection by countless doctors, I was thoroughly amused.

I would've tried to entertain myself and add fuel to this poor guy's awkward fire, but I suddenly realized the doctor had said that the tumors were shrinking.

Wait! What?

OK, Doc. No offense, but that needed to be the first thing out of your mouth. If there was good news, I needed her to get a running start and bust into the room like Kramer on *Seinfeld* with good news.

Resident Awkward enjoyed his spot in the corner of the room as the doctor and I discussed the results. That was right up until she made him actually do a physical exam. That was hilarious.

* * * * *

Husband and I enjoyed the high of decent results, followed by stable results, followed by mixed results for eight months. Mixed results meant some lesions were shrinking while others were growing. We made more trips across the state and started another oral medication – which kept me out of the infusion room and gave us some time back for living our lives. It gave us a chance to get our heads above water and to start talking about creating a life, literally.

We started discussing our options to pull the kiddos out of the freezer.

'Beautiful, beautiful boy'

There we were, at a Starbuck's on I-35 between Austin and Waco, waiting to meet the lady who we hoped would be the gestational carrier of our child.

After being told years earlier that we didn't need to waste the money to freeze embryos, we were now thankful we had listened to our guts and not to the doctors. Months before the recurrence of my cancer, I had shot up in bed with the decision laid firmly on my mind and heart: I wasn't going to carry our child. I firmly believed I shouldn't get pregnant.

I had no medical backing to support my decision, and I knew this decision came with a physical and emotional cost. It was met with some resistance at first as Husband hadn't yet gotten used to these epiphanies that came to me in the middle of the night. But now, here we were at Stage 4, and it all made sense.

Friends told him that I would be missing out on bonding with the baby and that it was a bad idea. Eventually, I pointed out that I would be no different than a dad. A dad didn't carry a baby. A dad didn't nurse. But the love a dad had for his child was no different from a mom's. There was just too much pressure on what role was socially acceptable for a woman. My ability to carry a baby had no bearing on my ability to be a good mother.

Husband and I had spent many a night talking and praying and thinking about whether we should take the next step. We had plenty of time idling on I-35 to discuss the pros and cons. We had many hard conversations about what would happen if I passed away.

Would this still be what he wanted if I wasn't here?

Would he be okay being a single parent?

These were tough questions that no one else we knew seemed to have to answer. I didn't know any non-cancer friends who had to have these conversations. Why didn't they have to talk about what would happen if one of them passed away or was hurt in a car wreck or if they later got divorced? Those things could also result in a single-parent situation.

Why was it so different for us that we had to have all of these conversations? The difference was that while anyone could step off a curb and get hit by a bus, I was there standing in the middle of the road, with traffic coming my way.

I wrestled with the decision and about what role I would play in my child's life. How long would I be here? Would he or she resent me if I was gone, knowing that I had consciously chosen to bring him/her into the world unsure if I would be able to watch him/her grow up? Let's just say it would be a boy, for the sake of discussion. If I didn't make it, would he know who I was?

I thought about what kind of woman might fill my shoes if I wasn't here. My sister-in-law was fairly influential in Husband's life, so I made sure to have a sidebar discussion with her about acceptable and unacceptable replacements for me. She accepted my terms.

These thoughts were constantly on my mind, but strangers and friends alike added commentary, some of it unsolicited. I thought about all the things I could teach him in whatever time I was given. I thought about teaching him to stand strong in adversity and to fight for his dreams and how to value each day. I wanted to teach him how to laugh. I didn't know what it would sound like, and I looked forward to his giggles. But

I could teach him how to laugh with his whole heart, to immerse himself in a moment and feel a laugh down in the belly of his soul. I had a laugh people could hear across a building and know it was me. (That's for better or for worse.) I wanted our child to have that same laugh.

In the end, after much discussion, we decided that we wanted to pursue our dream of having a family. Husband said he wanted a part of me whether I was here or not, so we began the interesting task of people-shopping – searching for the right carrier.

As I've mentioned, I'm quite the shopper. I could find a deal on a great pair of heels and a handbag with my eyes closed. However, this shopping for people was outside of my comfort zone. What exactly did you look for in an "oven" anyway? The youngest person might be the absolute best, or she might not understand the gravity of the situation.

In the course of choosing a surrogate, some prospects welcomed our involvement with the process. Others indicated that they would call when we could come pick up the baby. Some included photos that made me doubt their judgment. This online human shopping was new to me. Profiles would show up in my in-box. I'd read their thoughtful or hasty answers and peruse the photos they would send.

I didn't know what we were looking for, but we were burning through them as quickly as the agency could send them. For quite a while, I didn't see anyone I even wanted to meet whom I would trust to carry our child.

* * * * *

On February 2, 2014, we were in Dallas after a scan. We were at my sister-in-law's house after a celebratory dinner for good scan results on a new medication. Fatigue was setting in so I ran upstairs to lie down on the bed to get my second wind. This was a regular part of life at that time. I'd "ghost" a party for just a quick 15 minutes to lie down in silence and just play on my phone before returning.

It was then that I saw the profile come into my in-box. There she was.

There she was with her thoughtfully worded answers, with the best of intentions to help another couple become a family just as she had been blessed with her own. There were the beautiful photos of her and her husband and children. There she was.

My gut, which was the only thing with a consistent opinion, told me she was it.

My heart nearly skipped out of my chest as I bounded down the stairs and announced to Husband that this was it. It was her. Still begrudgingly unappreciative of my impulsive gut-decisions, Husband was leery. He read the profile and agreed she was someone we should meet, but he was not ready to make the call.

"Let's meet her first and see," he said.

Polly Positive and I had switched roles. I could sense his frustration that I had already made my decision before we even met her. I had learned to trust my gut, and my gut was leaping for joy!

I couldn't type fast enough to e-mail the agency back that night to say, "Yes, we'd like to meet her as soon as possible."

Anyway, this is how we found ourselves at a Starbuck's on I-35 later that month. The owner of the agency – who had been a surrogate herself – met us at Starbuck's, and we made small talk as we waited for our prospective surrogate to arrive.

We had no idea how this would go or what our surrogate, named Melissa O'Hare, would be like. Would she be a healthy eater? Would she smoke when she was pregnant? Yes, we'd have a legal agreement that would allow us to seek damages if she smoked, but that wouldn't change the impact on the baby.

Would she allow us to be a part of the process, or would she call us only when the baby was born?

And the biggest fear that haunted me: What would she say about my health? Would she hear our story and turn around and walk right out the door? Would she hear the words "Stage 4" and shut the conversation down, thinking we were selfish and irresponsible?

When she walked in, I sighed with relief. She was beautiful and had a kind smile. She walked with ease. She had a new baby with her.

My mind raced. Maybe she didn't know our timeline. Would she want to sign up for carrying our child so soon after carrying her own?

After the brief introductions and niceties, we looked at some photo albums Melissa had pulled together to show us her beautiful family. After that, the rapid-fire questions began. The owner of the agency helped guide our questions into these unchartered waters. As you can imagine, once again, we didn't know what we didn't know. We had only been married three months when we stumbled into cancer. We never had time to discuss questions surrounding childbirth. We never thought a third party would weigh in on these decisions normally made between a husband and a wife. It might have behooved us to have conferred about these topics before meeting Melissa, but we were just balls of nervous energy.

Would we ask to terminate the pregnancy if there were complications with the baby? Would we have multiples? What if Melissa got pregnant with two, but she only wanted to keep one? How healthy would she be during the pregnancy? Was her husband on board? What did he and their kids think about her carrying a baby for someone else? Would we do disease testing? These questions were just the tip of the iceberg in this process.

In the State of Texas, per gestational carrier laws, while the baby was ours once he or she hit the ground, up until the child was born the carrier could make any decision she wanted regarding her body and health, regardless of how it impacted the baby. She could wake up on a Tuesday and decide she didn't want to be a carrier anymore and our only recourse would be to recoup our money. That made the selections process more difficult. Though it was still a gamble, we had to at least feel that we were on the same page.

The other Starbuck's patrons had no idea how many life-changing decisions were being made at our table. We knew that there had to be a frank discussion of my health. We feared that this might be a deal-breaker. It wasn't. In fact, Melissa and her husband had had similar conversations. Prior to his deployment to a combat zone, they had decided to have another child. This was a fresh breath of understanding that we greatly appreciated.

When we left, we felt confident that Melissa was the one. Then the self-doubt and insecurities set in. What if she didn't like us? We were amicable and charming – or at least we thought so. What was there not to like?

We waited on pins and needles until we heard from the agency. Melissa liked us, too!

We were going to try to have a baby.

* * * * *

I continued to take my six pills a day and adjust to the side effects of this new medication. It appeared that the drug company was actually serious about the label on the side of the bottle advising that the medication be taken with food. It caused stomatitis, which, unlike what it sounds like, actually refers to mouth sores. I kept a big jar of salt at my desk to help with these sores. I had to avoid anything citrus or acidic, which was problematic since I loved all things lime, at least with my vodka. But the biggest side effect of all was the Palmar-Plantar Erythrodysesthesia, what is commonly called hand-foot syndrome. This was another side effect grossly underestimated by the Internet, doctors and nurses alike.

Just like the ole "quick prick and a burn" understatement regarding my lymph node biopsy, this medicine label described the side effects merely as "redness similar to a sunburn," and "a sensation of tingling or burning" and "calluses and blisters." These made it sound like I had a spring break on some beach with the mild casualties of too much flip-flop wearing and drinking in the sun. A more accurate description was that the pain would ebb and flow, but there would be periods when my hands hurt so badly that it brought me to tears even to make the bed. The sheer texture of the sheets felt like my hands were being split right open. There were mornings when it hurt to put my clothes on. My hands radiated heat and glowed red – all except the centers of the palms, which were always bright white hearts. A portion of the drug exited the body through the capillaries in the hands and feet, leaving them irritated. I experimented with every lotion I could find to ease the burning, but to no avail.

The medication added more complications to my high heel wearing – beyond dodging obstacles and sheer coordination issues. The calluses on my feet were painful to walk on, and the heels put more pressure on the balls of my feet. Unfortunately, the open capillaries kept me from pedicures due to risk of infection.

On a side note, if ever there was a time to pursue a life of crime, this was it. The calluses and redness took away any semblance of a fingerprint.

* * * * *

After the legalities of our surrogate arrangement were

agreed upon and paperwork finalized, we met with the fertility doctor who had been "babysitting our children," as it were, for the past four years. After the initial consultation, the awkwardness ensued.

Now, Husband has a knack for making an awkward situation more awkward. He overcompensates to put people at ease using commentary and jokes, but, in turn, tends to make everyone in the room feel more awkward. He's the guy who high-fives the waiter or hugs the stranger we just met. It's one of his most endearing qualities and one reason why everybody loves him – but it makes people like me with personal-space issues cringe. Imagine the possibilities for awkwardness with Husband in the room while our surrogate is about to have a vaginal ultrasound. Consider that stirrups are employed for this procedure.

There she was, naked from the waist down, in a situation that makes most women cringe even without an audience. Now, there are two strangers in the room, including one male trying to make her laugh and fist-bump her while she grasps desperately at the sides of her paper gown.

Fortuitously, Husband had never been with me for a doctor's appointment involving the stirrups. This left him ill-prepared for what was about to occur. I gave him a quick explanation of the process and pointed out the appropriate place for him to stand. What happened next was like kicking someone underneath the table who responds cluelessly with "Stop kicking me" loud enough for the other guests to hear.

"I'm okay here," he said.

"No, really, you need to stand over here," I pointed out.

This dialogue went on for a minute until his eyes got big as he finally realized that he did indeed need to be standing where I had directed. Luckily, I saved him from further embarrassment just in the nick of time.

Melissa couldn't have been more selfless. Not only was

she onboard to get pregnant to help fulfill *our* dreams, but the program came with the inconvenience of hormone treatments and their side effects plus the long drive from Waco to Austin as we prepared for the procedure.

(If you're not from Texas, you probably wouldn't know that stretch of I-35 is the worst construction site in the state. I-35 runs from just shy of Canada to just shy of Mexico and is the main north-south artery bisecting our state. To the east, Texas has water, to the west, little to none. The contractors had been working on this stretch of road for more than ten years. There was no end in sight to this construction process, so much so that the State started a marketing campaign, for the small fortune of $82,000 for one month, featuring billboards that said "One day, you're going to love I-35.")

With only seven embryos and no possibilities of more, we decided to implant just one. Four months after our initial meeting, we all convened at the hospital for the day. We didn't know what to expect and were so excited when Melissa and the doctor invited us to join them in the room to see everything happen. Husband was all in, but I was leery.

Eleven days later we found out it didn't take. Husband was heartbroken, as was Melissa. I was fine. I knew I never did anything the easy way. I had held back. I knew that I would be excited if and when it actually happened. We talked seriously about the next transplant. The doctor was hesitant. He even suggested that we consider another surrogate. My gut told me to stay the course. After much cajoling, the doctor agreed to put in two embryos to up our odds.

On July 25, I met Melissa at the hospital again. It was just us ladies this time. The doctor brought the images of the two kids in question. They were ready to roll. These guys were already on the way out of their protective membranes, ready to find a new home. We had always wanted twins. Would this be our red letter day?

*　*　*　*　*

After the implantation, Husband and I boarded a plane to Alaska to visit some friends. There we felt closer to the Earth and so small in the world. Because the sun shone all day long, we weren't sure what time it was when we received a text from Melissa. The text showed a pregnancy test – and it was positive! She was so excited that she just couldn't wait. A few days later, she sent a photo, this one with a stronger, more defined line. It looked pretty certain that she was pregnant.

A girlfriend of mine had told me it was tradition to buy the baby a gift at this point, so we snuck around and secured a pair of Alaskan moccasins for each possible baby, quietly celebrating between ourselves. It was a fun little secret just between us.

When we returned, we headed to the doctor's office, and he confirmed that Melissa was, without a doubt, pregnant. It was surreal.

Time stood still. In that moment, there was no cancer, no pain, no constant press of anxiety. We were going to be parents. We were going to start the family we always dreamed of.

In a moment of weakness, I told Husband he could pick wherever he wanted to eat for lunch to celebrate. I was blinded by excitement and didn't realize he had decided to capitalize on my delirium until we pulled up into the Golden Corral parking lot. Food in mass portions grosses me out. This was only amplified by all the people sitting on the curb and peering in the windows as they waited impatiently for this all-you-can-eat-buffet to open. Once the masses of asses banged down the door, we walked in to celebrate one of the most important moments of our lives – with lunch at Golden Corral.

*　*　*　*　*

Since we didn't have the opportunity to have a "Hey, we're having a baby" announcement, due to the medically orchestrated nature of the pregnancy, we had a gender-reveal party. It was really just an excuse to have cupcakes and some drinks. Since I wasn't pregnant, I could partake in the celebration as well!

There were a lot of people in our home ready to find out if it was a girl or a boy. The cupcakes – which revealed a blue filling when our guests bit into them – signaled that it was boy.

I was especially excited that our amazing surrogate and her children were among our guests. It was important to me to make sure these children were involved in the process and understood the selflessness of what their mother was doing.

While there was a lot of time between this celebration and the arrival of the baby, there was much to be done to prepare. Our surrogate typically delivered early, and there was legal work to do to ensure our names would be on the birth certificate when the baby was born. That meant added pressure to find a name as we wouldn't be able to make any last-minute changes. Fortunately, time in the cancer car, our white BMW, provided plenty of time to bounce names back and forth. It wasn't going to be easy. I liked more modern names and Husband liked the names of old dead country singers.

Out of time and out of choices, we started back at the letter "A," looking at the meanings of names to hopefully get some guidance. By the time we got to the letter "E," I felt this was going to be impossible. But I pushed on:

"What about Evan? It means 'God is gracious,' 'young warrior,' and 'rock.' "

Husband paused. This was the first time in all the names we had flipped through that any of them elicited a pause. It wasn't anything like any name either of us had planned for our son, but the meaning rang true. Given our story, my fight and the lengths we went to to get this little guy into the world, everything about the meaning was perfect. God had graciously blessed us with an amazing gestational carrier, a phenomenal medical team and the wherewithal to freeze embryos against all recommendations. Our boy was going to learn to be a warrior and a rock by watching me fight like hell to stay here on this earth to be with him and his dad.

There was no question. His name would be Evan.

We had kept the name a secret, except from Melissa and her family. They were delighted to rub her stomach and talk to our baby throughout the pregnancy. Since I wasn't feeling the physical pressures of pregnancy, my internal clock was out of sync. At one appointment in January, Melissa asked me how the nursery was going. I replied with a deer-in-the-headlights look, "Nursery?"

It was January. It wasn't going at all! She reminded me of her tendency toward early delivery dates, and I swung by the Sherwin Williams store on the way back to Austin and began calling every Babies 'r Us in search of the furniture. Husband started a two-week marathon of painting and repainting. With my micro-management skills, the nursery came together in relatively short order.

* * * * *

I asked my best friend what I would miss out on by not having been pregnant.

"Nothing," she said. "The only problem is that you aren't going to have any life-preparation time. You're going to be out at a bar and then you're going to have a baby."

And she was right. We had been out with friends the night before. When I woke up to get dressed for work, I checked my phone, which had a few nonchalant texts from Melissa. As usual, she was calm, cool and collected. Her texts played down any issues, but there was a casual comment about overnight contractions. She felt we had plenty of time.

That morning at work we were releasing a new section of home sites for sale and I had three appointments. I looked to Husband for guidance on whether I should go to work. It sounded like we still had a little time, so I headed to work in hopes of knocking out a few sales.

I arrived at work in a torrential downpour. I shouldn't have been surprised. Years of selling homes had taught me that people want to walk home sites only when it's raining. *Oh, it's raining, you say? Let's go to a model home park and drag some poor sales associate through the rain with no real intention of buying a home.* (At least this time, these people were legit. I had their money.)

I had back-to-back appointments and had explained to my clients the urgency of my situation. I told them we were going to need to make some decisions and fast. I wasn't pressure-selling them. They had had months to prepare for this moment and to review their selections. All I should have had to do was fill in the information and send them the contract.

But nothing went as I had hoped. No one seemed to really understand my unorthodox predicament, nor should they. I wasn't pregnant, after all. It's not like I was going to go into labor. After standing in the wind and rain, with the buyer agonizing over every decision, I did it all again with the next client.

There were quite a few logistical challenges that added some kinks to my plans – other than just wanting to be there for the birth of our son! Location, location, location. While these clients couldn't decide which home site they wanted without my traipsing back and forth in the rain between sites, this baby was coming into the world in Waco, Texas. That's in that cozy little part of I-35 we call Hell. On a good day, it would take an hour and a half to get there from our house; my job added at least 20 minutes to that.

Believe it or not, our distance from Waco was the least of our problems. All those months of paperwork had made it so that once Evan took his first breath, no one could take him but Husband or I. The legalities were standard procedure to protect the genetic parents in the event a gestational carrier decided she wanted to keep the baby – something we weren't concerned about in the least.

What we were concerned about was neither of us being there to get him. Then what would they do with him? Husband wanted to wait for me to get home so we could go pick up our child together – you know, like normal people do! I kept telling Husband no, that he just needed to get there. Someone needed to be there to claim our baby, and clearly it wasn't going to be me.

My blood pressure began to rise as my clients agonized over their exterior paint selections. I finally looked at them and told them to e-mail me what they decided. I told them I'd send them the contract later.

I threw my muddy rain boots in the trunk, changed shoes and drove as fast as the rain allowed. Getting in a car wreck wasn't going to help my objective. When I finally arrived, I ran back to the room where Melissa was waiting. She had been so sweet. Somehow, she had waited on me. She had been adamant that I be there when the baby came.

We had three minutes to spare.

Now, I had gone to hospitals when friends gave birth. But "gave birth" and "at birth" are two different concepts: Melissa was having a C-section.

When they handed me the baby, I nearly freaked out. Totally pink and wrinkled, I could see no indication that he even had eyes. Then, he opened them. I saw their blueness and broke down in tears.

The experience became even more surreal, if that could be possible, when the hospital personnel let us just walk out of the operating room with the baby. By now family and friends awaited their first peek at the little one whom we all would call the "miracle baby." He truly was that in more ways than one.

Because it was a caesarean delivery, our carrier had her own convalescence to consider. We were exhausted, but we kept running back and forth between our room and hers. I was terribly concerned about any postpartum depression that she might have. This was when her genuineness showed through the most. She assured us she would be fine. She was just so happy for us.

Since the baby had to be in the nursery for some period of time, we did what all Texans do: We went and ate Mexican food. We also had a chance to get to know Melissa's husband, who made his own sacrifices to enable us to have a child. Then, we worked out the details of getting Melissa's breast milk from Waco to Austin. Sometimes there would be milk runs up I- 35; other times she'd pack it in dry ice and ship it to us.

Just who would do this for another person? Our amazing carrier, that's who!

After three days in the hospital, the nurses got used to finding Husband asleep in the hospital bed and me dozing lightly on the couch. It was good to have the roles reversed for once.

The return trip down I-35 had to be the most tense drive of our collective lives. Husband was Captain Safety with hands at ten and two. But I badgered him constantly about his speed. We had a passenger on board!

Like most new parents, we were totally sleep-deprived for the first several nights. We remained glued to the baby monitor, counting his every breath.

We had been home only a few days when something disturbing happened: I threw up. Was this some kind of very late morning sickness that I somehow contracted by osmosis? No, a quick trip to the doctor advised us that I, the germaphobe, had contracted norovirus while at the most sterile of all places, the hospital. For the next two weeks, I crawled from bedroom to bathroom unable to be around my son while I was sick. Cancer anxiety was enough but now I worried that my son and I would never bond. How could this be happening?

The virus finally left my body. Things settled down and Evan became my greatest treasure.

*   *   *   *   *

Tumor markers are a kind of weekly way to measure the status of one's cancer. A simple blood test is all that's necessary to get this number. Higher numbers are bad; lower numbers are good. So, you can only imagine my shock when my number went up 1,000 percent in one week.

We had worked out an arrangement with my oncologist in Dallas to have my blood drawn in Austin for convenience. Who could fault the logic? For a while everything went as planned. The results were faxed to Dallas. We would review the results periodically while avoiding unnecessary trips on I-35. Then the 1,000 percent surprise occurred.

What did that mean? Was this it? Was I dying? How long did I have? What happened?

And, oh, yeah, the results came in late Friday afternoon, just before the weekend, but you knew they would.

Every effort to compose myself failed. E-mails and calls to the doctor were not answered. Yes, I understand doctors need to have their own lives as well. In my line of work, I took my customers' calls on my days off. Why couldn't the doctors extend the same courtesy? I had Stage 4 cancer, a terminal disease. Return the damn call!

At wit's end on Monday, we did something we had never done before: We headed to Dallas to my oncologist's office without an appointment. Prior to leaving home, I called the office and spoke with the nurse. They had the test results, but they had no appointment time for me that day. I told her we were headed their way, and that if I was to die, it might as well be in their waiting room.

We got there before the doctor's first appointment, thinking that just maybe we could get squeezed in. I mean things like that have happened before...somewhere, I am sure. We waited and waited and waited.

Finally, after 5 o'clock, we were admitted into the examining room.

"What is all the drama for?" the doctor asked.

That was her greeting. With that simple act of kindness, I tried to explain, but I was nearly speechless. She gave me another blood test; the numbers were in line with the prior month's numbers. I wasn't dying, at least not today, unless the stress killed me.

This did provoke an interesting discussion with Husband on the drive back to Austin. It turned out that the blood test I took the week before had been sent to a different lab in Austin than the one we ordinarily used. I quickly instructed my doctor in Austin to never, ever, never use that other lab again. The story circulated among the Austin cancer community. However, even so, you had to wonder why or how there possibly could be such a discrepancy in the readings between the two labs.

Lesson learned: All labs are not created equal. If you ever find yourself on this path, you'll hear a lot about "trending results" as an indicator of what's going on in your body. For consistency, make sure your doctors are using the same lab each and every time. (Maybe I still do have a shot at a medical degree, no?)

To add to the fun, for me, tumor markers eventually became less relevant. We were told that they were no longer important with my new treatment. Naturally, this did not mean I would no longer be subject to the joy that comes from pulling bloodwork.

Track 9

'In my hour of darkness'

The numbers kept inching up, so we started our whirlwind trips across the state to find out what the next steps would be when the treatment stopped working.

I just had a great scan which showed regression of the cancer, but the bloodwork readings weren't adding up. We thought we'd start getting our ducks in a row, driving back and forth to various facilities to see what trial options were available.

We returned to a facility we had consulted before. It was one that did a phenomenal job creating a spa-like environment. It was pristine. I could eat off the floors – if I could muster up an appetite to eat anything. Everywhere I turned I saw fish tanks and water fountains. The facility produced a level of calm, not the norm in the hustle and bustle of cancer centers – that is, until I turned the corner into the cattle call that was the lab facility. I woke from my Zen state by walking smack into a waiting room reminiscent of the Department of Public Safety. There was not a chair available in the room. How had they hidden this amongst all the serenity?

I wanted to let out a *moo* and see if it garnered a few laughs, but a few years into cancer I realized that not many others appreciated my sarcasm and jokes. I had a tight little circle of friends who, along with Husband, had equally twisted senses of humor.

In five years, I'd seen advances in waiting room etiquette. Slow advances, but advances nonetheless. In five years of sitting in waiting rooms, we'd advanced from regular sign-in sheets, to restaurant buzzers, to ticker tapes notifying us if the doctor was running behind, to online check-ins, iPad log-ins and text message updates notifying me when my doctor was ready to see me. Across six treatment facilities, I saw that they slowly tried to improve the patient waiting experience. It dawned on me that an entire generation was being left behind, unable to be notified of their appointments unless they had a smart phone.

The spa-like experience was the highlight of the trip. Unfortunately, we waited hours on end for them to receive and review my records. Communication between hospitals was asinine. I had already signed every form for privacy to allow any doctor to talk to another about me and share records, but inevitably there was always another form that provided a stalemate. Five years of medical records were caught up in the bureaucracy of HIPPA.

I was trying to save my life! I didn't have time to untangle myself from all their red tape. And let's be honest: Everyone in the world had my Social Security number, notes about my disease and, for good measure, the original liver biopsy report that the doctor had "lost" along with my tumor block (the actual tissue taken in the biopsy). Yes, let me repeat, the doctor had lost my painfully acquired tumor block.

There was nothing that wasn't "out there," HIPPA or not. I had collected so many HIPPA forms every time I checked into the doctor's office that I just threw them away as soon as I walked away from the counter. *Yea, yea, yea.* You supposedly have this fictitious guise of protecting my privacy, but I'm sure the government knows everything that is going on in my body, if only from the complaints they likely received from my insurance company about this pain-in-the-ass patient.

I could've done with a little dialed-back HIPPA and a little more cooperation from the medical profession. Chemotherapy and side effects weren't enough. Cross-communication was impossible. I wasn't sure if it was just arrogance that doctors didn't want to share patient information or if it was simply "the system," but even discs with my scans were rendered useless. A PDF is a PDF. A JPEG is a JPEG. I carried my bag of discs around to every doctor and not one could open the disc of another.

The only system that seemed to be working at any of these clinics was the billing system! I couldn't get a return call or e-mail. I couldn't reach a nurse for a question. I couldn't get an appointment scheduled. They'd promise to schedule me by Tuesday at the latest and Tuesday would come and go with no call. Sometimes you had to wait and see if the "doctor would agree to see you."

What? They can do that?

For me, the communication between doctor and patients in Cancerland was null and void, with a few exceptions. But, re-gardless of the facility, I would get a bill before I even left the parking lot.

Back to the good news being good, because it could have been so much worse. Those rogue cancer cells had chosen to set up shop in my liver. The liver is chock full of blood, thus, it is a nice warm spot for cancer, meaning it would stay put (I hoped) and not metastasize to other organs. Regrettably, most chemos currently available are processed through the liver. Chemo is basically poison. We would later realize how poisonous it was.

For the present, I had a great liver, except for the cancer that resided there. It was currently impacting roughly two percent of my liver. I had 100 percent of my liver function.

* * * * *

Cancer wasn't killing me, but anxiety was.

I was on this teeter-totter between waiting and anxiety. You waited on tests, scans, doctors, return calls, and the decisions of every possible stranger, bureaucrat and insurance representative. The waiting compounded the anxiety. I have always been punctual and conscientious. That did not keep me from worrying about the possibility of missing an appointment or not getting a chance to talk to a doctor.

The scans showed that I had five lesions.

Well, let's talk about that.

I started with five, two bigs and three smalls. Scans, in theory, ought to be the most accurate method of determining just exactly what cancer is doing inside your body. Logic would suggest that conclusion. But for that to really be the case, I would need to be positioned exactly in the same spot for every consecutive scan. The scanning device would also have to be in the exact same spot, same angle, same calibration. See where I'm going with this? Plus, and probably most importantly, my scans should be read by the same doctor each and every time.

You already know the answer, and do you know why you already know the answer? Because you are a logical person!

Tumors move, some die, some grow. Scans show that. But to get a consistent handle on my lesions was difficult, if not impossible. I would have thought that the same doctor would have read my scan, for the sake of consistency. I didn't care if he wasn't the valedictorian of his class. Let's just have some consistency.

We were at a large research hospital. This meant students. What if they just assigned my scan to the class dunce? What I am saying is, even the scans created doubt.

The largest lesions stopped responding to chemo, but the other three, if there still were three, were responding. One of the larger lesions was positioned in a place that enhanced the likelihood that cancer could escape my liver and spread to other organs.

Yes, cue anxiety.

We started exploring the possibility of radiating the two larger lesions. At this point they were about three to five centimeters in diameter. And, at this point, my liver was healthy and functioning. Radiation made sense to those of us without a medical degree.

When I mention large research institution, you should read "bureaucracy." To me, it was just another hospital. I did not realize that it had its own rule book. Before radiation could be considered, it had to be approved by a committee. Heretofore, I had gotten accustomed to having to clear my treatments through my insurance carrier. By now they had assigned a real live person to my case, which I thought was pretty enlightened for a bureaucracy. I could not fathom why "the best of the best" had to consult with anyone.

Wasn't this going to take a lot of time?

Sure it was. How much time, no one could say, but no one could say how much time I had. So let's just sit back and let me try to handle the stress.

Cue the Xanax refill, please.

The committee suggested that surgical removal of the two large lesions was not an option. We would need to return to a chemo form of treatment.

It was hard for us and our doctor to understand how a committee could overrule what we all agreed was the best course of action. It would have been helpful if modern medicine had developed an additional chemo that was processed elsewhere – like in my exceptionally healthy kidneys. There was risk everywhere. Ultimately, Husband and I decided, along with my oncologist, that radiation made the most sense.

*   *   *   *   *

Being the amateurs in this game, Husband and I were a little disturbed at the multiplicity of opinions concerning the next step in our game of life. At a breast cancer fundraiser, I had met some people connected with a California institution. We thought a trip to the West Coast would be in order to seek another opinion. Of course, this would take more time, and time was becoming more precious. I would have to be off chemo for six weeks before starting radiation. Husband and I put everything on hold – Remember, we are both in real estate sales and appointments are our livelihood – to focus on what might be a life-saving opportunity. The institution confirmed this was the correct approach.

By now, all the usual games we used to pass the time on I-35 had grown very old. Husband decided that it would be a great idea to stop in every little town along the way and buy a lottery ticket. Husband felt that we were due for some good luck. I was skeptical. This idea did spark the imagination, however, as it would in most people. We talked for hours about how we could spend the money.

I wanted to buy new infusion chairs for the entire state of Texas. The chairs would have to be made so that cancer patients could actually get out of them on their own. Cancer takes a lot from you – dignity, control and freedom. You ought to at least be able to extract yourself from the chair without the assistance of someone else. It was humiliating. My new model would have a built-in heater and perhaps a massage feature. If you are going to have to spend so much time in the chair you should at least be comfortable.

We knew the drill. I arrived at the hospital – in Dallas, not California – with five lesions. They gave me the usual gown, and as usual it would have fit the Fifth Fleet.

Let's digress for a moment and talk about wardrobe again.

I understand that there are cost savings to buying things in bulk, but there has to be a happy medium. Literally, for almost every scan, I find myself in a pair of one-size-fits-all scrubs, falling down to the floor if left to their own devices.

No amount of double or triple knotting will keep this strip tease from happening. I have had to resort to tying the actual pants in a knot, and once even utilizing vet wrap!

The radiation itself was quick and painless, but it would be spread over a two-week period. The fatigue increased as the procedure went forward. The results were anything but quick and painless.

Let me give you the layman's summary.

The two big lesions were gone, yippee! I figured five lesions minus two equaled three, at best. After radiation, I had 25 small lesions that had not been visible before. Now radiation did not explode the big guys. That is not how it works. However, no one could really explain the 25 small lesions. If modern science ever had an "Oh, shit!" moment, this was it. Between the lines, there was a subtle concern that radiation had obliterated a great deal more of my liver than what was expected. The liver is supposed to regenerate itself. No one would hazard a guess if this would happen or if so, how long it would take. My liver now looked like it was splatter-painted with cancer. Cancer had always been in both lobes of the liver. Now it was there uniformly throughout.

From this point forward we were to be limited to systemic chemo. Hormonal treatments would no longer be available. I would have to be infused for the rest of my life.

Track 10

'Always something there to remind me'

My blood began to boil. *Swish. Swish. Swish.* How did something so innocent and happy cause so much anger deep down in my soul?

I remembered this feeling from the first time I went through chemo, wearing a bandana to the gym, jogging behind some girl with a swishy ponytail. I'd had a swishy ponytail my whole life. I never thought anything about it. I'd throw my hair in a ponytail, a braid, a knot on my head, curl it, cut it, whatever, but I never gave much thought to it at all.

It surely wasn't my identity. It was just hair, and I happened to have a lot of it.

But as I faced my second and third bouts of my hair falling out, I started to realize it was more of my identity than I thought. Now that I was confronted with the reality that I was never again going to have a swishy ponytail, it bothered me. It laughed and pointed at me. It was part of the Mean Girl Club: *Look at me, Courtney. You'll never have this again.*

I watched girls pull at it and struggle with it being in their face and flip it over their shoulder with annoyance. I would give anything to be annoyed with my hair again. I'd give anything to be face to face with the tragedy of not having a rubber band when I needed one.

I thought it would get easier each time. I thought I would

lose any attachment to this trivial superficial thing called hair. But every time my hair fell out, it became more painful. Every time it fell out, the knife twisted deeper. Every time, it broke my heart a little more and reminded me that I was never getting off this train – unless there was a crash with no survivors, which was kind of a crappy either/or scenario.

Swish. Swish. Swish. It was just a visible reminder of a life that would never be mine again. No more would I be able to make the simple choice of having the hairstyle I wanted.

Yes, it was just hair. But it was so much more. It was a visible reminder that never again would my life be mine, free to live without a noose around my neck. To add insult to injury, all these men were running around with their man-buns. I live in Austin, Texas. There are a whole lot of man-buns in our town.

We had a customer whom we affectionately referred to as either Knight Rider or Michael Bolton because he appropriately drove a Corvette, wore "jorts" (jean shorts) as his permanent uniform, and had long flowing hair – which I'm pretty positive was permed. I never saw this guy without wind in his hair. Somehow his hair must have had this magnetic field that attracted a wind vortex wherever he went. I ran into him at work, in the neighborhood and at restaurants. Every single time I saw him, the wind was just perfect so that he looked like he was on stage at a Guns 'n Roses concert with the fans blowing his hair back. Knight Rider had hair, but not me.

Sure, I had great wigs. To outsiders, I looked perfectly normal. I'd mastered drawing-on my eyebrows; I was fine as long as my husband could keep from wiping them off for a good laugh. I was alive. I just didn't have hair. It was so easy for the rest of the world to say "It's just hair."

But it was just one more thing to remind me of cancer. There were the scars. The misshapen, mangled breasts. The fatigue. The memory loss. The lack of estrogen and the resulting diminished sex drive.

There were all these reminders of a life that I couldn't control – of the me that I'd never be again. I recognized that I needed to grieve the old me and embrace the new me, but I couldn't for the life of me figure out how. I'd always been able to do everything – to do everything for everyone else and then take on some extra load. It must be the German in me. I was an emotional pack mule.

The mourning of the loss of the old me was debilitating. I was a Type A personality if ever there was one. *Get on the train or get out of the way. You can help if you want to, but candidly, I don't really need your help. I can do it on my own.*

Yet, there I was, bound and gagged with no control.

I finally decided that this was God's way of throwing my deadly sin of pride in my face. Of all the deadly sins – avarice, envy, wrath, sloth, gluttony, lust and pride, a.k.a hubris – the one I was most guilty of was excessive pride.

Yep, Hubris and I went way back. We were old friends that didn't go anywhere without the other.

I came out of the womb pissed off that they didn't have me dressed in a cute outfit. By six years old, Hubris and I made sure that our pajamas were color-coordinated and well accessorized. By third grade, Hubris and I tried to sell my parents on why I needed this extra turtleneck simply for lounging around the house. By fourth grade, I had turned color-coordinated Converse high-tops into a mainstay with our red, yellow and green plaid jumpers. In junior high and high school, I was part of the most well-accessorized basketball team in the Brazos Valley.

Hubris and I picked out my cute shoes to attend chemo and double-checked that our toes were freshly painted before any of my surgeries. Hubris helped me do my makeup even on days where I felt like death warmed over. Yet there I was, constantly losing and re-growing my hair and eyebrows and eyelashes; Hubris and I were on the brink.

And therein lies the kicker. I wore wigs in large part because

I was vain. I had always been vain. I didn't want to look like a cancer patient or look sick in every photo that was taken of me. I wanted to be remembered in photos as the vibrant person I used to be. I didn't want to see pity in people's eyes when they saw me. I just wanted to feel normal.

And at the very same time I'd have days when I just wanted to chunk my wig at someone and tell them to stop being such an asshole. I wanted to be treated just like everyone else. But I also wanted people to understand what I dealt with every single day – with physical, mental and emotional limitations. After five years, I finally wanted a little credit.

On a particularly hard day, I had to deal with a snarky sales agent at a department store, and it took everything I had not to tell her off. *Look lady. I understand you're having a bad day. I understand that some customer was probably rude or your boss pissed you off, but do you want to hear about a really bad day?*

But I held my tongue. I considered doing a victory lap around the mall while singing the theme song from *Rocky* as I celebrated this great feat of self-control. On some days, I wanted to look customers in the face and say: *I get it. There is a small, miniscule paint chip in the wall or an old coke can in the home that is not yet completed that you do not technically own yet. I get it. It's a travesty. I'll write an e-mail to the CEO while I'm in che-mo-ther-a-py!*

I worked in a customer service sales job. It didn't matter what type of day I had. My job was to put a smile on my face and not let the customers feel anything but excitement in the purchase of their new homes. I prided myself on my strength and steady positive attitude, but the very thought that my attitude had shifted was a shot to my pride. Though I had always been a sympathetic person, my compassion waned as I fell into the trap I had cautioned others against: comparing sob stories.

It had taken five years, five years of my brushing cancer off my back like it was nothing. Five years of my "playing the hand I was dealt." This was the hand that I had to muster up a poker face to play – but I had to play it and do my damnedest to win the pot. Because the pot was winner-takes-all. Was I going to live and see my son grow up, or was I going to fold?

* * * * *

As I rounded the corner to five years, I had grown tired and found myself in a position I never thought I'd be in, ready to wave the white flag. I finally found myself stuck in the muck and the mire. I was pissed that I had let it beat me.

Well, hello, Hubris. It's nice to see you again.

I couldn't even quit right. Even in defeat, my pride mustered up the strength to lift its head before being slammed face down on the floor. It had taken five years, but I felt like cancer had finally broken my spirit. I mentally replayed the scene from *Unbroken* when Louis Zamperini holds a six-foot pole above his head for hours on end. Cancer was my six-foot pole. I held it high above my head, unwavering but for a few staggered steps with the burden of both the disease and having to cheer on my cheerleaders. But it had finally broken me.

I'm not sure if I can pinpoint the moment when my legs began to shake and my knees began to buckle. I'd venture to say it was somewhere in those long 15 months of no progress and even some regression. The fissures in my liver probably started when I naively let myself fall into the black hole of the hope that the radiation was going to work on the two remaining liver lesions and I'd finally arrive at this elusive "No Evidence of Disease" place that people talked about. But instead shit hit the fan. The tremors likely started right about the time my friend Holley died; we were in the Pink Ribbon Cowgirls together.

I couldn't seem to shake the anger. I'm sure I could have paid a psychologist to tell me it was a result of my internalizing things and trying to be everything to everyone and that all my guilt was unfounded. *Thank you, self. You saved me $150.*

Hanging out with my "normal" friends was increasingly difficult. Hanging out with my survivor friends who weren't Stage 4 was increasingly difficult. Actually, hanging out with anyone was hard. I struggled with not having anything to say. I never wanted to be a burden on anyone or a downer, but I had nothing to contribute that was anything other than cancer.

What have you been up to lately?

Cancer.

How are you feeling?

Eh.

Things are getting better though, right?

Sure.

Sure was equally as dangerous when used by a cancer patient as when a wife says it to a husband.

I'm going to take the trash out later. Is that okay?

Sure.

Sure was a four-letter word that packed a punch. It was laden with sarcasm and hidden meaning. I no longer had the energy to "fake it 'til you make it" in vain attempts to make others comfortable. No one really wanted to hear how I was feeling. No one wanted to live through the defeats and statistics. I didn't blame them. I didn't want to either. I couldn't nod and smile and dismiss the severity of the treatments as I had done before. It just took too much energy.

Actually, I feel like crap. Thank you for asking. I knew no one wanted to hear that, and I knew before I even said it that they wouldn't know how to respond, but keeping up the appearance that this had been a cakewalk was exhausting. I'd been the cheerleader for my cheerleaders for too long. I was too tired to pretend I wasn't tired. And it's not like I had the ponytail to go with my cheerleading outfit anymore anyway.

I didn't want to be handled with kid gloves. I wanted to be useful and offer advice. I wanted to feel needed. I wanted to feel normal and be the friend I would have been before. There were moments when I'd look at friends and acquaintances in disbelief as they complained to me about a relatively minis- cule problem, oblivious to their audience.

I started to look within and figure out how in the hell I was going to get myself out of this hole. I searched for anything that would help me claw my way out. My dad always told me I needed to "shrink my back yard." I'd roll my eyes like daugh- ters do because I didn't really have that big of a back yard, literally or figuratively. I had family, work and cancer. I'd love to kick cancer out of my back yard, but the Big Guy Upstairs apparently hadn't looked in the suggestion box in a while.

Work? Well, it was work, and I had cancer. They had me by the phenomenal insurance. They couldn't quit me and I couldn't quit them. I knew how fortunate I was to have a supportive employer who thought enough of his employees to provide such great insurance. I'd heard story after story of women declaring bankruptcy because of cancer and not being able to get their next treatment because they couldn't afford it. I surely didn't want to be in that number.

I didn't necessarily want to quit my job. My issue was the sheer claustrophobia that my life was causing. I was a Type A control freak and I had absolutely no control of what lie before me. I felt trapped in Cancerland and trapped in the moment. I felt the overwhelming despair of finally giving in because I didn't have any choice in the matter.

The kicker was that once I vocalized to my family that I was kicking around this idea of a leave of absence, everyone started gnawing at me constantly like a dog with a bone. It was like I showed weakness and they jumped on it to tear it apart. They had the best of intentions. Everyone wanted me to be stress-free and healthy, but they couldn't grasp that their "help" was adding more and more pressure. Their effort to take the pressure out of my life was just adding to the pressure.

In a world where many people would do anything to not have to work, some people thought I was insane. I had a terminal disease and qualified for disability, but I was kicking and screaming to stay employed. No one could grasp that this was just one more thing that cancer wanted to take from me. I always wanted to be a career woman. I wasn't a little girl who dreamed of weddings and white picket fences and children running around the yard. I was a girl who dreamed of climbing the corporate ladder and making my own way and being respected by my peers.

I agreed that I needed to find a new path. It was simply that I wanted to be the one to choose it. It had been five years since I had a real choice. Granted, Husband would have loved it if I would pick a restaurant, but even that wasn't a real choice. Everything tasted like crap and while I wasn't some raging alcoholic, cancer had even taken away happy hour.

Cancer had taken my breasts, my hair several times over, my fertility, my ability to carry my own child, my cognitive function, my carefree spirit. It had taken away my ability to plan a vacation in the distance as I wasn't sure what treatment I'd be on. I couldn't make plans to do anything beyond that very week or sometimes that day.

Want to go to a music festival in October?

I don't know. It's July. I might be in treatment.

I'm getting married in Ireland. Would you guys like to go?

Hell yea, we would! But we will have to wait until the last minute to book because I don't know where I'll be in my treatment.

Want to go to dinner Friday?

Yes, but I'll have to let you know how I feel that day after chemotherapy and work.

People gradually stopped asking me to attend things, unaware that every fiber of my being wanted to be as carefree as them. I wasn't noncommittal because I was blowing them off. It was just the world I now lived in. I never knew from one

(Continued)

I'm hoping for some good news while waiting in my oncologist's office for the results of a scan, in October of 2015.

My storyboard as a lifer – The lifers are a group of women with Stage 4 cancer who support one another, raise breast cancer awareness via social media and other means, and push for a cure.

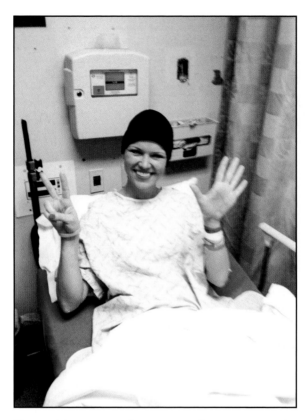

I'm awaiting my seventh surgery, my first mastectomy, in March of 2012.

In September of 2014, I was on an oral chemo regimen, along with multiple vitamins, anti-nausea pills, and calcium to try to preserve bone strength.

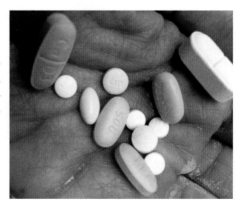

A short while before my first mastectomy, I arranged a
photography session, in June of 2011, so I'd have pictures
of how I looked pre-cancer.

What a difference eight
months makes! How
I looked just prior to
our wedding compared
with my appearance
midway through my
first chemotherapy
treatments.

Before
(March 2011)

After
(November 2011)

That's one happy mother with one precious baby, in May of 2015.

– Photo by Brian and Amanda Rogers, Austin Newborn & Maternity Photography

Family portrait, October 2015 – Courtney, Roger and little Evan...

Courtney, Roger and Evan with our family dogs, Duke, a yellow lab (left), and Allie, our German Shepherd, in October of 2016. (Our other dog, Heidi, also a German Shepherd, died of cancer in 2014.)

Courtney and Roger with our little "buckaroo," Evan, in October of 2016...

– Photos by Brian and Amanda Rogers, Austin Newborn & Maternity Photography

Photo by Brian and Amanda Rogers, Austin Newborn & Maternity Photography

My last photo was taken in October of 2016. I wanted to go out in heels and makeup, and I did.

minute to the next if the pressure would lift and I'd have a moment of reprieve.

I began to feel the guilt trip walls closing in again. If I'd muster up the energy to see one friend, social media ensured that all my other friends were perturbed I hadn't seen them. If somehow I managed to respond to a text message, I'd receive a whole slew of messages indicating so-and-so had heard from me. I was barely breathing. I felt like I was on life support gasping for air.

Cancer took away so many parts of my identity that I wasn't even sure who I was anymore. I knew I needed less stress. I knew I needed more time with my family and friends. I knew I needed more time really living, not worrying about quotas or placating irate customers. It wasn't about what I knew or didn't know. It was about what I felt. My brain and my heart were totally disconnected. I hung on for dear life to something I wasn't even sure I still gave a damn about, but something that was the very last trace of the person I had been: my job.

* * * * *

Working was the source of constant stress. I couldn't perform my job duties like I had done before – which was both frustrating and disheartening. Also, the idea of *not* working was a source of stress. It made me bitter that I would have to give up my career because of cancer. Everyone else makes their own choices. My Facebook news-feed was full of my friends using their time off for actual vacations instead of medical appointments. What a novel concept.

I cheered everyone on in their lives as they followed their hopes and dreams. I stood on the sideline with balloons and signs urging them forward toward their next adventure. But there I was, standing still, hanging out with my buddy, cancer.

My least favorite phrase reverberated in my mind. I wanted

my cake and I wanted to eat it, too. No shit. What idiot came up with that saying? Who wanted to have a piece of cake just to stare at it? It was the dumbest phrase I had ever heard, and it had weaseled its way into the dark crevices of my mind.

I wanted to work, but I didn't want the stress. I feared my friends and coworkers would forget about me when I wasn't there. It felt like I was writing myself out of my own life. It was like looking into the future and seeing what it would be like if I didn't make it. I would be forgotten before I was even gone. It felt like I was standing on the outside of a party I hadn't been invited to. Somehow I had gotten left off the list of invitees.

I wanted to be a good friend, but I wanted people to realize what I was going through. I didn't want to be treated as a cancer patient, but I wanted an "atta girl" for what I had been through and continued to face. There was this constant struggle between my selfless self and my selfish self.

I felt isolated and left behind. When was it going to be my turn? I was stuck on an island, claustrophobic in my own life and in my own skin.

And that's when the hives started.

Even during a mundane task, my fingernails would idly find their way to my skin, clawing desperately to stop the itching. No amount of Benadryl or cortisone would offer relief. The doctors and nurses tried to isolate the side effects of my medications. Maybe this was an allergic reaction to the chemotherapy? Maybe it was a side effect of a medication I was on to treat a side effect of another medication?

Or maybe I was just itching from the inside out.

All the scratching caused more itching and slowly my body was covered in hives. I would claw at my skin until I would bleed. Days turned into a week and then I landed myself in the Emergency Room with a panic attack.

'Oh, what a night!'

We had been asleep for only about an hour when I woke up and I couldn't feel my face.

It wasn't my first time with this feeling. Things like this happened only in the middle of the night. They never happened during the day when I had access to both my doctor and childcare.

The last time I couldn't feel my face in the middle of the night, shortly after I was diagnosed with Stage 4, I found myself in the E.R. with a transient ischemic attack, or TIA. A TIA is a mini-stroke. The doctor said something about stress? Shocker.

Now, here I was again, in the middle of the night, and I couldn't feel my face. Before waking the bear, I sat up in bed and did all the stroke tests on myself. *F.A.S.T.* I touched my *face* as I smiled. I stuck out my *arms* and tried to touch my nose with both hands. I babbled quietly to myself.

My exam was rudely interrupted when my brain started spinning around in my skull. Then my eyeballs started spinning around in their sockets. I rolled my eyes to the left and then they kept spinning in that direction. Crap! They wouldn't stop spinning in that direction. I was like one of the characters from *Beetlejuice*. I knew I should wake Husband, but I thought I would go to the bathroom first and see if I could shake myself out of this fog.

Nope. I ran into the walls and felt like I was going to die.

I held my face still as I looked into the mirror. My eyeballs weren't spinning. I was just losing my mind. With physical proof to the contrary, I tried, to no avail, to reassure myself that my eyes were not spinning around in their sockets like you'd see in a cartoon.

I made it back to bed and tried to focus on my breathing. I took deep breaths and tried to calm myself down. Crap! My chest tightened from side to side.

What the hell was happening?

I knew it wasn't a heart attack, but I was pretty sure I was dying.

I finally woke Husband and quickly informed him that I was dying as he was wiping the sleep from his eyes. My communication style really didn't give people a whole lot of adjustment time. He attempted to get up to speed on my symptoms.

I was hung up on the fact that I couldn't remember the rest of the words to the Aggie War Hymn, "Hullabaloo, Caneck!" I must have been having a stroke! I was a diehard Aggie. Why was my mind stuck on repeat, constantly playing, *Caneck, Caneck?* There were literally no words coming. *Caneck. Caneck. Caneck.*

I began to shake uncontrollably.

Husband assured me I was not shaking. *Yes, I was, dammit!* I was shaking all over! Husband laid his arm across my chest and repeated that I was not shaking. *Yes, I was!* My insides were shaking and my chest was cramping up like I was tightening my muscles as tight as I possibly could. Husband tried to hold me to calm me down. At some point, I became aware that he was back in a sleepy haze, nuzzling into my side and kissing on my neck. *Was he seriously trying to get some action? Dude!* Here I was dying and he was trying to make his move. I made a mental note to strangle him later if I made it out alive.

Crap! My facial numbness was back. My jaw was tingling and painful, like I had been blowing up balloons. I started my stroke tests over again, and my mind raced as I struggled to see the time on the clock. It had been too long!

Husband said it had been only a few minutes since I woke him up. He was the crazy one. Not only did he think this was an appropriate time to try and get lucky, but he had clearly lost his sense of time. It had been forever. It had been a way longer "forever" than Dr. X said it would take to re-grow my nice, long hair. Terrified, I told Husband that I loved him, in case I didn't make it. That sprang him into gear.

"Get up! Let's go to the hospital," he said.

"I don't know. Are you sure it hasn't been that long?" I replied.

"OK, get in the shower. I think you're having a panic attack," he said.

So, I got in the shower despite the overwhelming terror that I was going to die there. Shit! Drowning was my worst fear; I had almost drowned as a kid. I was a grown-ass woman and I was going to drown in the shower!

Before I got in the shower, Husband told me to text our neighbor, the one with the heat-sensing goggles. He was a one-stop shop. He was police, fire and EMS. Great! Not only was I going to die in the shower, now this guy I'd been friends with since my twenties was going to have to give me CPR while I was naked in the shower. This was going to be awkward. We had really rounded the bases quickly and upped the ante from using goggles to inspect my boobs to my being full-on naked!

You are who you are. Let it be known that whoever you were in life, you will be in death – or something that feels like death. I came into this world sarcastic and vain and I was going to go out sarcastic and vain. I got in the shower and curled up on the floor and began to dry heave. Sarcasm mixed with fear, and I thought pretty seriously about the fact that I wasn't seeing any Pearly Gates or bright lights. It appeared that in spite of all my good intentions on this Earth, I was Southbound, if you get my meaning.

When the symptoms didn't subside after my shower, Husband announced we were going to the hospital. My maternal instincts kicked in. What were we going to do with our son? Germs! There are tons of germs at the hospital.

"Don't wake him up. I'll be fine," I blurted out. But, really, I knew I was going to be anything but fine.

I wanted to call the neighbors to come watch him, but I knew Husband had determined I had lost my mind and didn't want to wake the neighbors for my trip to Crazytown. He was being very calm, but was noticeably annoyed. I couldn't understand why he was exasperated. It wasn't like I was having a good time! He looked at me like, "This girl has lost her freaking mind. *Shuuuure*, your eyeballs are spinning around in their sockets. Let's go get your eyes checked out and then I'll drive you over to the loony bin to pick out a nice coordinating straight jacket."

I didn't care what he thought. I really thought I was dying. We loaded Evan in the car and headed to the E.R.

It was a particularly slow night when we arrived and the nurse took me back immediately. Husband and our son met us in the examining room. Despite the sleep time interruption, Evan was calm, never fazed by anything. I was reviewing my symptoms with the nurse, and the second I said "Stage 4 cancer," I got first-class treatment. The scans were ordered quickly, under the assumption I might have cancer in my brain.

If there was a moment to love in all of this - which, let's be honest, there really wasn't - it was when our baby got a little restless. He watched patiently as they took my vitals and accessed my port. When he began to fidget, Husband laid him down next to me in bed. Evan's cheek was on my shoulder, and he looked up at me.

"Mama."

Finally, I could breathe.

Let's back up quickly to my port. Bless this little guy's heart, but I'm positive that nurse had never accessed a port, ever. I could tell he was terrified. He had to use my port because five years of poking and prodding had created a mess of scar tissue around my veins. I was 90 percent positive he left the room to consult with Dr. Google about how to access a port, or the doctor's equivalent of Dr. Google. (Years of watching *Grey's Anatomy* led me to believe this existed. It also led me to believe that there was a copious amount of doctor-sex being had in the on-call rooms.)

So, the guy came back in the room and asked me if I had a regular port or a power port. I answered him that it was a power port. He left again. Dr. Google to the rescue. Mind you, I could have told him how to access it or even done it myself had I been of sound mind. There were three little bumps on the power port. It was the braille version of "insert needle here." In the center of the bumps, it felt like little erasers. To access the port, you pushed a needle through the eraser and drained all the blood you needed.

That, my friends, is not what he did. I don't know what he did, but it wasn't that. It had never hurt this much, and blood was barely trickling out into the tube. For tonight's little episode, he didn't need just one tube of blood, he needed many. I was a bleeder – such a bleeder that once a nurse made me order a bracelet saying I was a bleed risk because I covered an entire pillow with blood in 45 seconds. There was no way this guy did it correctly. Finally, he got enough blood that he stopped sweating and left the room.

In the middle of this debacle, the EKG technician appeared and was visibly annoyed that the blood dude didn't have his shit together. He rolled his eyes as he wheeled me away. We headed down the hall for scans.

After a battery of tests, I was diagnosed with panic attacks and a pulmonary embolism – a blood clot in my lung. Which came first was undetermined. I was placed on blood thinners to dissolve the clot. I was slightly concerned, given my propensity for bleeding.

Time to turn the page

I never liked taking medicine. I mean B.C. – Before Cancer. As a child, I was pretty sickly most of the time. Swollen glands were routine; weekly trips to an allergist were common. For whatever reason, this doctor always insisted on prescribing a Z-Pack, a strong antibiotic. I may have eaten my weight in Z-Packs. They seem to have had little or no effect. Thus, my early experience with prescribed medicine was something less than fulfilling. I suspected a weak immune system.

With cancer, there was a virtual avalanche of drugs. I did not want to be over-medicated. I continued my daily regimen of eating healthy foods. I tried to avoid any kind of booster shot, unless I absolutely needed it to continue with my chemo.

All things being said, one day I reached the lofty summit of 15 pills per day. I would line them up in double rows. Do you have any idea how much water you have to drink to swallow 15 pills? A lot! Xanax, Ambien, multi-vitamins, codeine, and Benadryl all tripped across my flight path. Then, there were the steroids, which were used with chemo to buffer any possible allergic reaction. They made me very emotional. I was offered them routinely while in the blue infusion chair. I could see Husband cringe when I took them.

We cancer people often refer to our state of existence as "cancer brain" or "chemo brain." This means that we are really not ourselves. We do not know what we are doing, nor do we remember what we did. Some experiences feel almost like out-of-body events. Steroids gave me tremendous mood swings. Mix this with the fact that I was now going through a premature form of menopause, and you can imagine the result. I sometimes knew I was acting crazy and would repeatedly tell Husband how sorry I was. That did not stop the craziness, though.

Being affixed to an infusion chair did not help things. The first day of chemo is always the longest; figure eight hours on average – a full work day. By the time I worked down through most of the regimen, it would be in the five-hour range. It was still no walk in the park.

Playing in the background was the constant need to be vigilant. Was this the correct chemo being administered? Had Husband or I confirmed it? Was there a trial that might work? Would we have to change doctors and/or hospitals?

The stress of it all was just unbearable; yet, what alternative did I have? I wanted to live. I still had dreams. Was I scared? You bet I was.

The calming voice was that of Dr. H. She had plans. She thought more than one step ahead. She was available, shared her cell phone number, became invested in me as a person, and actually returned calls. Plus – and this was a big plus – she wore heels.

We started thinking about some of the PD1 trials. These are basically a group of tests that focus on immunotherapy. Simply stated, this treatment is designed to fight cancer with your body's own immune system. We thought this might be our Holy Grail, our ultimate answer. Radiation had proven to be a disaster for me, and we had few options left.

We were running out of tools in our "tool box."

Track 13

'Take another little piece of my heart...'

A nd with a click of the mouse, it was done: I hit "send" on the e-mail request for short-term disability.

That click signaled farewell to another piece of my identity as the person I was before; it ended the hopes and dreams I had for what I wanted my life to be like when I grew up. Now, my blessings weren't lost on me, but that didn't change the sadness I felt in my heart. I was so fortunate to have a wonderfully supportive company and phenomenal benefits. The manager wanted me to focus on my health and said my work would be there when I wanted to return, in whatever capacity. I couldn't have worked for a better company. I was fortunate to have had the opportunity to step away from work and spend time with my family and friends. I would finally have time to put my health first and focus on healing. But these blessings were made bittersweet by the knowledge that this was just another part of me that I had conceded to cancer.

An innocent suggestion by my manager, with no ill-intent, that I take my personal belongings when I left the office sent me into a tailspin of upset and despair. That small comment yanked away any iota of power I clung to. Sure, I knew I could always come back if I wanted to, but psychologically it assured my seat on the bench as others moved on in my place. It reinforced my fear that I was being written out of my own life.

Around this time, one of my friends called me with a scare. She had gotten "that call" – that "come in and let's see if we are going to change your life forever" call. Having someone like me in your life is a double-edged sword. It's great to have me for questions on dark days such as this one, to help you down the path like others helped me. But my presence makes it real. It makes it real that someone so young could actually have cancer.

As I sat there with her creating a diversion, something I'm particularly adept at, it dawned on me that I was now that person. I was the one who was supposed to have the right thing to say if the doctor said she had cancer. But I must admit: I was blank. What in the hell was I going to say if it was cancer? How was I going to ensure I didn't say something equally stupid as the things that had been said to me in pivotal moments like this one when I got the shocking news in June of 2011?

As I watched the ultrasound tech prep her, my heart started pounding louder and louder. I felt my pulse in my head. Not only was it surreal, being in this room, re-living what had started this shit show of my life nearly five years earlier, but also it was stressful. I had just enough medical knowledge to be dangerous. As the tech rolled the ultrasound device around over my friend's breast, I saw it immediately. I saw exactly what they were looking at and why they had called her back in. Shit! I adjusted my chair and leaned in to study the images more closely, doing my best to appear nonchalant for my friend, like I was just leaning in to comfort her. *OK, I don't think it's cancer,* I concluded with my non-medical degree. Fortunately, the mass they identified was benign. What a wonderful relief for us both!

* * * * *

I routinely received calls from friends or friends of friends who had just been diagnosed with cancer. The Pink Ribbon Cowgirls, of which I am a member, is a tremendous support group. Support goes two ways: They supported me and I, in turn, supported them. But, Husband, family and friends had admonished me for too often becoming someone's new best phone-a-friend. After five years, I was starting to hear their warnings.

I never wanted cancer to dictate the course of my life, and certainly not the direction of the lives of Husband, family and friends. The leave of absence from my job was a blatant reminder that it had done just that.

I had been burning my life at both ends. I would race to work after chemo. Who does that? I wasn't trying to be a martyr. I was just stubborn, trying to be "normal." But, now it was obvious that I had not given my best effort towards what was most important, namely fighting cancer. In my effort to be the best I could be, I had failed to give my body a chance to rest, to recuperate and to fight its own internal battle.

I had been a good member of the cancer sorority. But now I had to find my own people. I had to prioritize my time for family and friends and, hopefully, squeeze in some time for me.

* * * * *

While we are talking about time for me, girls, we need to have a frank discussion about Tupperware.

Yes, I said Tupperware.

I know women who value Tupperware like a family heirloom. Friends would often bring food over, which was always greatly appreciated. But, I could barely keep my own dishes washed. There were days that they just did not get washed. I was just too damn tired. If you bring Tupperware and/or your grandma's heirloom china platter, I have to wash it, care for it, protect it and try, with chemo brain, to remember whose it was. Plus, I have to return it to you.

One of our male friends is a champion cooker of all things barbeque. He often brought over wonderful brisket. I love this guy. First, the brisket is world class and he brought it in an aluminum tray. You know, the kind you just throw away. Guys don't like to wash dishes. Girls, learn something from the guys: Don't bring any food on or in something that you want back. Enough said.

I'm glad I got that off my chest.

*   *   *   *   *

My leave of absence from work provoked a lot of second-guessing. Certainly, I would now have more time available to me. Maybe, hopefully, doors to a cure would open for me. Should I wait patiently (not in my nature) for a door to open, knowing the person on the other side is just moseying along to open it? When do you just kick the damn door down? The second-guessing grew and grew. Should I have taken my leave sooner? Was I giving up and planning for defeat? Would I research myself into an early grave?

I concluded my battle against cancer had to come first. Trying to maintain the "old me," the pre-cancer me, was not working. It was a bitter pill to swallow, but I took heart in making plans for a normal schedule with Husband and Evan.

Dreams of weekend trips, family fun and more time with family and friends lifted my spirit.

Track 14

Farewell, Holley, my friend

Holley was our leader. We all looked up to her. Diagnosed with Stage 3 metastatic breast cancer at age 38, she influenced each one of us to our core.

Holley had been in the vanguard of raising the profile of metastatic breast cancer. She made the public service announcements and did the interviews, all while she was dying.

She often asked me what kind of legacy I wanted to leave. I had never thought about a legacy. I had been so busy trying to hurry and grow up, get a job, and do all of the things I was supposed to do. Then Holley strongly suggested the legacy I should leave. She said I simply *must* write a book, and that she would read it many, many times over.

When Holley was near the end of her life, her family invited several of us in the sisterhood who were near and dear to Holley to come to their house and join them in a meal and say our good-byes. It dawned on me as we sat in the living room talking about day-to-day life, this was anything but a normal visit. What was normal to our group wouldn't fly in the outside world. We had come together as sisters to support one another and to support the family and friends of a sister we loved so dearly, a sister who lay dying in the next room.

Holley and I had become dear friends. We had a unique bond, but, looking back, she probably had a unique bond with most everyone she met. She was a self-proclaimed introvert, but her million-watt smile lit up a room and welcomed everyone into her heart. She was so filled with life. But now the end was near as we each waited patiently to say our good-byes.

When it was my turn, I walked into her dimly lit room and shut the door. Those moments we shared were and always will remain between us, but I cherish them so. In some odd way we were lucky. Though we had carried the burden of living with death, we also had time to say our good-byes – something so many others without cancer couldn't do. When it was time for me to go, I held her hand and stood up and kissed her on the forehead.

"Safe travels, pretty girl."

I walked back out into the light, into conversations with these women who had become so comfortable with death. We did not welcome it with open arms, but it was a harsh reality that was part of our everyday lives. Where other friends talked primarily about work and husbands over margaritas, our conversations had no boundaries.

We had an unspoken understanding of both planning to live and planning to die. We could talk freely in a way we couldn't with our families. Others thought our planning to die was in some way giving up the will to live. For us it was anything but. We continued to fight like hell for every extra moment we could.

In a seamless stream of consciousness, we covered topics ranging from the silly things our husbands or children did that day to what we wanted at our funeral. We talked about our wishes for our families and friends after we were gone. We prepared one another for what battles we might face with our families once we had passed away. We divvied up responsibilities ranging from obituary writing, photo selection and family wrangling to who was in charge of making sure our spouses didn't move on with a barfly.

We laughed as we made the others swear to make sure we

weren't buried in some dumb outfit or that they didn't say something cheesy at our funeral. We laughed as we described how cool we wanted to be portrayed in our obituaries. To an outsider the conversations would have been morbid and inappropriate. We had the conversations our loved ones didn't want to have. An innocent bystander would have been appalled at how we conversed so flippantly over both our lives and our deaths.

But, the truth is, we were anything but flippant. We were just dealing with our reality the best way we could. We didn't laugh in the face of death; we laughed alongside it. We laughed because often there wasn't anything else we could do.

Having grown up in a private family of four, I never understood why a person would attend the funeral of an acquaintance. That seemed like an invasion of privacy, to intrude on such a personal moment in time - that is, until I attended my first sisterhood funeral, Holley's funeral. Guests flowed in constantly. Chair after chair after chair was filled with another pink sister. We held hands and wept. We embraced and shared laughs and memories.

As Holley's family turned to see the room behind them, they were lifted in that moment of grief by the sight of the many people in attendance - standing room only. The outpouring of love offered them some solace.

It was then that I started attending funerals - if not for myself, for the loved ones of the deceased.

Track 15

'All my trials, Lord, soon be over'

The numbers kept inching up. I had a good scan just weeks before, but something wasn't adding up. We had begun exploring next steps in anticipation of a change in my treatment, but we were just exploring. The good scan showed us we had some time.

A month later we ordered another scan and the exploration process became more urgent. Things were going in the wrong direction. How quickly things were changing.

Scan days are a necessary evil in Cancerland. Anxiety runs high for the patient as well as for her supporters.

The people at the front desk of the doctor's office underestimate their importance on these pivotal days. The way they greet you never goes unnoticed. The way they walk you back may throw you into a tailspin. You notice it if you normally go through the left door, but this time they're taking you in the right door.

Cancer makes you oddly superstitious. In a world where nothing is under control, if maybe wearing the same outfit or following the same pattern could garner some small feeling of control, then you do it. I am positive that the folks at the Dallas facility thought I had only an orange button-down shirt in my closet – right up until the day I had a bad scan, and then I started wearing all the other pieces in my wardrobe.

Cancer continued to eliminate my options. Words from the past kept coming back to mind: that each successive chemo treatment would offer a shorter respite. I found this to be all too true and was shocked at how quickly we were burning through our "tool box." It didn't help my situation that every chemo that had some chance of working for me was processed through my liver. It was anybody's guess how much more poison my liver could process. We had to start investigating trials. More importantly, we had to be mindful that if my liver functionality was too impaired I would not qualify for trials. No pressure there.

Husband, family and I constantly talked about trials vs. traditional therapy. We had decided early on that sticking with traditional treatment was the route we wanted to go as long as it was viable. Here we would at least have a baseline against which to measure the cancer's response to treatment. The clinical trials were something we planned to avoid, unless there were no other "good options."

In hindsight, I'm not sure this was the best strategy, but we made the decision on the information we had at the time.

I now had a striking sense that we were, in fact, out of "good options."

My Dallas and Austin oncologists started looking for trials that might work for me. All of the research hospitals listed existing or soon-to-be-offered trials. This was the easy part. The delicate part was twofold: First, you had to qualify by meeting their standards; then, the dicey part, you would have to be off chemo for some period of time.

The Dallas and Austin doctors thought that an androgen trial available in Dallas looked promising. The doctor in charge of the trial agreed. She was another "best of the best," only she traveled the world giving lectures about what she was doing. (Note to self: Would she have time for me?)

Husband and I had now come full circle. In fact, we found

ourselves in the same circular drive where we had met my dear friend, Dr. X. This is the same spot where I had collapsed in Husband's arms after this most memorable visit. The mastectomies were done here. But nothing had really changed. We had driven over three hours up I-35, which was, of course, still under construction. There never was any readily available parking, so we cruised the garages hoping for a spot. Alas, none was available, so we were forced to valet park yet again. *I have cancer! Can't you give me a tag or something? Couldn't you have a lot close by that said "terminal cases park here."*

I had assumed since this was the only trial available at the time that The Man Upstairs was sending me a message:

"Courtney, just walk through the door and follow the blinking light."

All the forms had been signed. Everyone was supposed to be able to see everything everyone else was doing. We live in an age of technology. Shouldn't all of this information be just a mouse click away? Despite the fact that I had answered each and every question many times before, I still got a world-class asinine question.

"Mrs. Lasater, are you pregnant?"

Well, sweetheart, why don't you just step outside and check the bio-waste dump. If you can locate my ovaries, ask them. I haven't seen them in quite a while.

I am pretty sure the file should indicate that I don't have any ovaries; seems like a major thing.

Unfortunately, the trial did not go well. In fact, my numbers spiked. Some called it "a flair." Flair, spike, whatever, I had to stop the trial. Our hopes were dashed, but no one would tell us what had happened, whether it worked on any of the cancer at all, or if it destroyed the remaining functioning portion of my liver.

I have never flunked a test in my life until this trial. It was humiliating and heartbreaking. It caused me to re-examine the attention and the care that I had received in my travels to Dallas up I-35 in pursuit of the "best of the best." When I looked around at my girlfriends who were also at Stage 4, I realized they had been under the care of my Austin oncologist since the recurrence of their cancer. They were stable in that lofty plateau called "No Evidence of Disease." The doctor who treated them was so close that I could have jogged to her office. How many miles had I put on the cancer car?

Perhaps the true "best of the best" had been in my back yard all along.

Track 16

There's no place like home

Whether I liked it or not, most doors were now closed to me. For five years, we had conscientiously researched every possible option to beat this cancer.

Once again we had made a trip to Houston. The facility, as always, was impressive. The lobby was as tranquil and serene as I had remembered it. I was not garbed in acres of paper or cloth. They gave me a robe. Imagine that, a robe. And it actually provided some sense of dignity and modesty. How long had robes been around?

My numbers were still in range, meaning that I qualified for the trial. However, once we went downstairs for the blood work, it was still like a cattle car operation. Now, I am not saying it wasn't a clean cattle car operation, but the urge to *moo* was almost overwhelming. It was like renewing your driver's license at the Department of Public Safety. Wait, have we talked about this before?

Soon after our run to Houston, we were back on the road and headed for San Antonio - to try to qualify for yet another immunotherapy trial. Now, I cannot say we were optimistic; optimism had been crushed way too many times by cancer.

But, we were glad to be going to San Antonio. All Texans have two favorite towns, their hometowns and San Antonio. Plus, my parents now lived in San Antonio.

Husband and I talked the whole way to San Antonio, not about cancer, not about the immunotherapy trial or the ever-decreasing number of options available to us. We talked about seeing my parents and their house. It is the most peaceful house I have ever been in, and I sell houses. I think, in the presence of our parents, we all become children again.

There is something peaceful about coming home to a meal cooked by Mom and sitting down talking with Dad. It feels normal, something I constantly strive for, and it always brings a smile to my face. Family and friends had become my safe haven.

We would stay in the upstairs bedroom off my dad's study. I just love it. One afternoon I excused myself to go lie down for a while. I never said that I was going to take a nap. Nap meant sleeping. I hadn't really slept for five years – except during operations. I could not sleep in Vegas, nor on that cruise. I could not even sleep in my own bedroom. Husband came up to check on me periodically and was surprised to see me sleeping.

When I awoke I was surprised that I'd fallen asleep. The room was awash in sunlight, the curtains were not closed, the digital clock was staring me right in the face. I cannot explain it. I was just so happy. The tranquility of the moment put me to sleep when nothing else could.

My parents had opened their home to us for the upcoming trial we hoped to start in San Antonio, and we looked forward to more of these moments. Of course, the purpose of the trip was to qualify for an immunotherapy trial. As I have previously stated, we were hopeful that the trial might trigger my questionable immune system and lead me to that coveted state of "No Evidence of Disease."

This institution, like every other one, insisted on doing their own blood work. The fact that these hospitals and doctors can now look at your existing records doesn't mean they are going to rely on them. Hell no! They are going to repeat everything that has been done before anyway.

We finished our visit with the doctors and headed back to Austin. On the way, we got the call. I didn't qualify for the trials in San Antonio. My numbers were now out of range. We had researched my way to an early grave.

Track 17

Going out in heels and makeup

The next little adventure in my trip through Cancer-land was the accumulation of fluid in my abdomen. This was causing a shortness of breath and an abundance of pain.

The culprit was my poorly functioning liver. Big surprise!

My doctor sent me to the hospital for an abdominal scan and a paracentesis. She saw the scan, read it and ordered that my abdomen be drained. One of my breast cancer sisters had alerted me to this possibility. The procedure gave me some immediate relief.

Curiously, after I was drained, they just let me walk out of the hospital by myself. There was not the usual ream of paper-work, nor any bill. I mean, how bad could it be?

The weekend passed and the fluid built up again. I got dressed Monday morning and headed back to the doctor for my appointment. Right off the bat, she started talking about liver enzymes and fluid buildup and catheters and the like. She talked about options and a hospital admission to get the fluid under control. She wasn't being very direct or very clear, but I got the message. My shoulders slumped in defeat as I knew where this was going. If this Hail Mary didn't work, my

163

liver would fail and I would die.

Husband wasn't catching on. He was talking about liver transplants and other treatments, right up until she looked him in the face and got his undivided attention.

"I'm going to need you to sit down," she said.

She wheeled in close and looked directly in his eyes. She told him that he needed to focus on being strong and being the best father he could be to our little boy.

I sat there stoically as she explained that there was no Plan B. She said she would do the best she could to restore liver function, but if it didn't work we needed to be prepared for this to be the end.

I needed to say my good-byes and make my arrangements, write letters to my son and help my family prepare for life here on Earth without me in it. We needed to have a plan for Evan, and we needed to have no regrets for anything left unsaid.

The doctor hugged us both and cried then left the room to make the arrangements to admit me to the hospital.

We walked next door to the hospital and sat on the couch crying as they finished the paperwork. I knew there was a real possibility that I'd never walk back out of those doors. My hand shook as I signed the admitting forms.

The nurse brought me a wheelchair to take me to my room, but I declined. While I may never walk out of here, I could walk in, so I was walking. I clung to Husband's shirt as I sobbed. He wrapped one arm around me as we walked down the hall, a hall I knew all too well. We were on the oncology floor, a floor where I had said good-bye to far too many friends. It was like walking the plank with a sword to my back.

I cried to Husband; I just didn't understand.

I had tried so hard to do it right. I tried to give it my all.

I tried to work and exercise and be a good wife and mother.

I tried to be positive and take it all on the chin.

I'd tried to fight cancer with grace and poise and never with a bitter heart. Yet here I was.

I had tried to be an open book and offer my guidance and comfort to anyone who heard the words "You have cancer."

On top of it all, I had poured my heart out into a book to help others through cancer, and it was all for naught. I'd gone on leave to focus on my health and the book and I wasn't even going to get a chance to finish it. I was so frustrated and heartbroken that I could hardly see straight.

I always believed in karma. I had tried so hard to put good karma out into the world. When was it going to be my turn to see it come back around?

I knew all too well that cancer wasn't a disease that played fair, and this death sentence proved it. This just wasn't fair.

I was shocked by the immediacy of it all. I guess in the few times I had seriously thought about death, I thought of it as a slow process. I thought I was going to see it coming. I thought I was going to have time to wrap things up and say my good-byes. While others might keel over from a heart attack, the one advantage of having cancer – if you want to call it that – is that I would get to see it coming, right? I wasn't going to go into a regularly scheduled office visit with a stomach ache and then never come home again.

It was difficult to make calls to friends and loved ones because I didn't really know what I was supposed to tell them. *I'm supposed to call and tell you good-bye, just in case, but hopefully I'll pull through, in which case I'm just being a drama queen.* I looked at my contact list, hesitant to hit send.

If I told anyone, did it seal my fate?

Would my friends roll their eyes if I pulled out of it?

On top of it all, it was my sister Brittany's birthday. Of all days my body could choose to be the center of attention! If I didn't make it, she'd forever remember her birthday as the day her sister called to tell her she was dying.

The hardest call to make was to my parents. They were going

to have to bury their daughter unless, by some miracle, my liver decided to live. I knew it was impossible for me to think of Evan burying his mom, so I understood how much it would hurt my parents.

I was now flying on sheer faith and will power. Beaten and downtrodden, I had to dig deep. In that instant, I went from a "C" to an "A" student-patient. If anyone could will herself out of death's grip, it would be me.

*   *   *   *   *

My sister was the first to get to the hospital. We hugged and talked, but there wasn't much to say. What would anyone say? We mostly talked about my fears for Evan. I was so scared that Evan wouldn't know who I was. He was only 18 months old. While I had known I was poorly accessorized with this noose around my neck when we chose to have him, I had always thought I would have more time to teach him. I thought I had more time for him to get to know me. I hoped he'd learn to love my laugh. I thought he'd be able to pick up my sarcasm. I thought he'd be able to hear my voice on a video and recognize it. I thought I'd be more of an influence on him. At 18 months, how long would it take for him to forget me? Would he even notice that I was gone, or would it be like I went on vacation one weekend and never came home?

Friends began to arrive. Ironically, many of them I never would have met if it weren't for cancer. The room was large. I guess the hospital knew I was one of the Cancer Girls. They had seen me enough as a visitor. Despite a less-than-stable liver, externally I still looked the same (well, maybe slightly more yellow). I sat in the bed, still looking like I was a part of this world, but not knowing how close I was to the next one.

I had been sitting in bed for hours before the nurse hooked me up to the medicine, but I had started feeling better long before the drip began.

Was this the calm before the storm? I always heard you get better before you get worse. Was I experiencing my body's last burst of energy before I kicked the bucket? I started eating; it was the first time in weeks that I had any sort of appetite.

The nurse who came to access my port and start the fluids was sweet. But she was nonchalant, like she didn't understand the seriousness of why I was there. To her, it was Tuesday. She haphazardly stuck the needle in, but it didn't seem to faze her when I yelled out for her to stop.

Something was wrong. I'd had my port accessed hundreds of times, all poorly in recent history, but hundreds of times nonetheless. Something was wrong. I started wheezing as it felt like it was burning in my chest. I didn't have any medical training, but I was positive I knew more about what it felt like to have a needle stuck into my chest than this nurse. She stopped briefly before trying again.

The second attempt had the same result. She didn't seem to even have a heart as she pulled the needle out and went in search of the head nurse. She was unapologetic and dismissive of my concerns. Eventually I stopped coughing and another nurse came in. There I was fighting for my life in the oncology ward and I was having to give directions to nurses. Insanity! This was the oncology floor!

* * * * *

Husband and I lay in the hospital bed that night talking about things a young couple in their thirties shouldn't have to talk about. It had been over five years since cancer first invaded our lives. When I was diagnosed with Stage 4 in October of 2013, the doctors gave me 24 to 36 months to live. It was now September of 2016. If I didn't make it out the doors, I had made it 35 months.

It dawned on me the arrogance I had. Never once had I felt that statistic was meant for me. I was younger and healthier. We caught it earlier. I was active. While we had written our wills, we had never gotten into the details of the final day as I really never thought we'd be here. And yet here we were. One by one, we made decisions about my final farewell: pallbearers, orange flowers, funny stories. We snuggled up together, playing songs on our iPhone, songs that we wanted to play at the funeral and the after-party.

Who would say my eulogy? I wanted it to be about memories of me living, not of me dying. I wanted to make sure that no one ever referred to me as having lost my fight to cancer. That would be insulting. It would imply I didn't fight like hell. It would imply I could've done more. It would imply I didn't have the will to scrape and claw and do everything I could to make it. I wanted my eulogy to say this:

> Her race is over. She crossed the finish line today and
> is at home with her Lord. She fought the good fight. She
> finished the race. She kept the faith. (2 Timothy 4:7).

I had no idea where I'd be buried, or if I'd be buried. It didn't matter to me. Once I was gone, I was gone. I had always wanted my body to be donated to science to see if anything I had been through could prevent someone else from walking in my footsteps. But was there anything left in me that was worth keeping? The physical act of a funeral was for those left behind. A memorial would have sufficed for me. All I cared about was that there was a damn big party when it was over. (Good luck with that, Husband. No pressure.)

It bothered me that I had left the house in disarray. I had just started my leave of absence from my job, and I was going to try to organize the shit show that had become my life. Five years of spending our days off on the road for doctor's appointments had left a cluttered mess of our house. I was going to leave this world with a messy house and my family and friends were going to have to go through all my crap.

Ladies, let's be honest. We all know the state of the house is a reflection on the wife. Husband couldn't grasp this point, but it wasn't lost on me that I hadn't had the chance to organize things. I remembered being a little girl when my grandmother passed away, and I helped sort her nail polishes. I started thinking about the in-progress projects I had at home – organizing my closet, decluttering the cabinets, repainting a couple of rooms, removing the back-bedroom crap for a garage sale. All these things were undone. Everything was undone.

In the evening, Husband and I had the hospital room to ourselves. But not really. During the day you practically had to beg for attention. But in the evening, the nurses routinely came in to check on me, flooding the room with fluorescent light. At home, even the blinking light on the cable TV box kept me awake. So I knew there was no way I would be able to sleep here. Another go-to-sleep option might have been to take a long, hot shower. Except, this hospital had no hot water. It had lukewarm water, sure, but that's not the same thing. Plus, there were only hand towels to dry off with – yes, hand towels.

*   *   *   *   *

Husband and I continued our futile Internet research for answers to my medical problems. Never one to delegate everything to the medical staff, we seized on every new word or unknown statement. It was very clear that we had left the arena where the fight against cancer was taking place. We were now somewhere else, focused on trying to restore some functionality to my liver. Medical people say you can survive if your liver is functioning at 25 percent of its capacity. Mine was short of that mark. I had been at 100 percent when my cancer recurred – before radiation. We suspected that I was now in the neighborhood of 15 percent. So where did the other 85 percent go? What percentage could be attributed to radiation? Chemo? We did not know. No one would hazard a guess. And it all may be a moot point in the near future anyway.

The new players were sodium and bilirubin. I got sodium. To us lay people, that means salt. To the medical community, it means sodium, although they would soon prescribe salt tablets for me. The other player, bilirubin, was new to me. It sounded like the name of a jazz singer, Billie Ruben. The more I read about bilirubin, the less I understood, but generally speaking it's a substance made through the normal breakdown of red blood cells.

* * * * *

Every hospital room that I have ever been in, whether as a patient or a visitor, had a fixture on the wall with a clear plastic container screwed onto it. Heretofore, I had never inquired about it, which may be unusual for someone with an enlarged sense of curiosity. In order to drain me of the fluid, without poking a new hole in my abdomen each time, they installed a catheter in my side. Basically, they could now attach a tube to the catheter and that thing on the wall would suck out the fluid. In theory, the tube was positioned where it would do the most good by draining the most fluid.

Now, let's give this some thought. I had already been the guinea pig for several nurses when it came to accessing my port, a fairly standard device for a cancer patient. Somewhere in the bowels of this hospital, there was a machine that created a vacuum strong enough to provide suction to every room in this hospital. That is a lot of suck in anyone's world. The only device that could regulate the force of suction was a little lever on the wall, plus the skill and experience of the operator. Since I was not equipped with a dipstick of any sort, it was anyone's guess how close I was to being completely drained. The tube inside me was lying directly against flesh and organs that had never been touched before by anything or anyone.

When the suction finished with the fluid, it just continued with whatever organ was close by. The pain was immediate and intense, so intense that I wanted to throw up and pass out at the same time. Husband would have to learn how to drain me if I was ever going to be released from the hospital. But, we did not have that contraption on the wall at our house. They would give us vacuum bottles, which are a good bit more difficult to regulate. Through trial, error and pain, we would learn how to manage the process the best we could.

* * * * *

The fluids given to me at the hospital stabilized my sodium level enough that the doctor released me to go home. I wanted desperately to leave the hospital and its lukewarm showers and small towels. The bilirubin level continued to go up. My liver was failing, but, at least for now, I would not die in the hospital. No matter what the circumstance, there is no place like home. I would be able to hold my son.

I refused to let myself think about the end for fear that it would somehow speed up the process.

Late in the evenings, since neither of us slept much anymore, Husband and I would lie in bed talking and watching whatever Hollywood thought would pass for entertainment. It's surprising how often Hollywood uses cancer as a theme or plot. These are supposed to be the creative geniuses of our time. They return to the same cancer dialogue so often that it becomes trite. We were trying to relax, but the plot line brought us right back to reality. The comic relief was the commercials that now raised "dry eye" to the level of a disease. *Sure that'll work. Could I trade you a little cancer for some dry eye?*

After a slightly restful weekend at home, we returned to the doctor's office. All of my levels were out of whack again. Back to the hospital we went. They showed us to a room. But I declined the room; one of my cancer friends had died in it. They proceeded to walk us a little further down the hall and opened the door to the room where Holley had died.

It was at this point that every ounce of stress, pain and anxiety that I had felt during the past five years collapsed upon me. The avalanche of cancer engulfed me right in front of an ordinary hospital room – except that this room was the place where an extraordinary woman took her last breath.

Then Husband and I stumbled into a vacant room nearby, and I had a total and complete meltdown. I could not be stoic any longer.

For this hospital stay, for however brief or long it might be, we restricted it to just family. Each morning at 6 a.m., I would hear the distinctive cadence of Dr. H's stiletto heels coming to see me. You have to love a woman in heels. It was all the motivation I needed to get up, take my shower and put on my makeup. Her job wasn't easy. We had developed more than a simple doctor-patient relationship. You sense these things. Giving me the bad news had to hurt her as much as it hurt me to hear it. I was glad that I got it from a real live human being who happened to be my doctor.

Nothing was going in my favor, she told me. I had a couple of weeks to live.

The hospital counselor came by. *Good Lord, what a difficult job!* I did not want to die in the hospital. I wanted to go home. They just needed to figure out how to make that happen. Usually, during the day, I was pretty much left to myself. Husband, my parents and I had the room to ourselves. My sister brought up my favorite salsa, which was a true treat. Well done, Britt!

Then, out of nowhere, a funeral director showed up. Husband and Dad, with some penetrating questions, had gotten the names of credible ones from the counselor.

I had always been quite the organizer. Parties, events of any sort, I enjoyed it. Now we sat discussing funerals, internment, orange flowers and cemeteries. We had not finalized any of that stuff, and I highly recommend that you do it early. There were decisions that would have to be made later. Dad had been through these things before; I was confident that he and Husband could handle the rest. For the moment, I just needed to exhale.

On the heels of the funeral director came hospice. Those visits were short, which was good because it was all a little overwhelming. In regard to a funeral, I believe when you are gone, you are gone. But I have learned that the services are expressions of sympathy and support for the grieving families. I was really more interested in where they were going to have the reception afterward. The entire episode was surreal. Who sits on a bed planning her own final arrangements with her husband and parents? We signed the release forms. I thought about refusing to sign another hospital form. I mean, what were they going to do to me? But best not to misbehave now. I was going home. I would not die in the hospital.

The rest of my time would be spent with family and a few close friends. I was growing weaker, but I still had things that I wanted to do. First, I wanted pictures taken with Husband, Evan and all of our family. Sure I was dying, but I did not look it. While I could still get dressed and put on my makeup, I wanted pictures – for my son and for my family. One last thing for them to remember me by...

We had friends who were photographers. On a moment's notice, they came to our house. We took wonderful pictures of Husband, Evan and me, our last photos as an Earthbound family. Every combination was taken. A one-on-one with me would be followed by a group shot. Of course, I got to see them before anyone else. I was very pleased.

There was one very poignant shot with my mom. In the blink of the camera's eye, as Mom kissed me, it captured the breaking of her heart. I saw it. I felt it. I am a mom as well.

* * * * *

The next day I was pretty spent. I still had things on my to-do list. Husband and I planned a slide show for the memorial. I had picked some pictures that I thought were suitable. There were many more to sort through. I hoped to write a short farewell as well as my obituary.

That morning, during my dad's time with me, I recognized that I was running out of time, so I asked him to write my obituary. He had written a tribute to me, just for me. It was touching, I cried through each lovely word. I cannot imagine what it takes to write your child's obituary.

During one visit, my sister, our parents and I sat on the bed together. It seemed odd in a way. Here we were, just the four of us, like it had been for so many years. We talked about all the wonderful pets we had. Even before moving to the country, we always had pets – pets with personality. None of them were forgotten. Each one brought back a flood of memories. Once grown and out on my own, I had a German Shepherd named Heidi, which I have previously mentioned. Heidi was discussed thoroughly. She had died of cancer about a year or so earlier. Odd, isn't it? She was going through what I was going through, all at the same time.

Although Husband and I were very happy to be back home, we were having a hard time accepting our new reality. We did have time to make sure nothing was left unsaid – which I realize is a blessing many aren't afforded. In between draining my abdomen and working through the outpouring of love and visitors stopping by our house, Husband and I were able to talk a lot about what I wanted for my funeral, for Evan, and for their future – a future that would include only a memory of me. We'd talked about it often since our beautiful son first graced our lives. We also managed to take some great videos for Husband and Evan to enjoy further down the road.

These were conversations I never wanted to have, but I was aware enough to be grateful for the opportunity. Whether you have a terminal disease or not, I would encourage you to take the time to make the little memories precious. Take lots of videos and photos – and include a healthy dose of sarcasm whenever possible!

I had asked the doctor how it would all end. You knew I would. Once again, I was given the "good news." I always got the good news, because the bad news was so horrific. Since my liver was failing, there would be no pain. I would remain lucid. I would start sleeping more and for longer periods until I left you all.

Oh, and back to the photo session for a moment... That evening, Husband, Evan and I went to the photographer's farm for more photos. I could no longer walk by myself. Husband supported me in every shot and as we walked. That is, until we took the picture for my obituary. In that one I stood as straight as I could – yes, in heels – for the last time. I wanted to be remembered as alive until the very end.

The time of my departure is at hand. I have fought the good fight. I have finished the race. I have kept the faith.
(2 Timothy 4: 6, 7)

One beautiful, courageous woman

By Roger Lasater,
Courtney's husband

On October 18, 2016, Courtney passed away at 4:14 p.m. We'd been blessed in the fact that we knew the end was coming.

"Blessed" is a strange term to use, I suppose, but by that I mean we had the opportunity to make sure nothing was left unsaid, no regrets, no "If only I'd have told him/her...."

Over the last few weeks of her life, we were flooded with friends and family, and Court was afforded the gift of being able to say her good-byes. We were able to spend quality time with our son Evan and record videos and audio books and just lie back in bed and read him stories. She wrote a few special letters to be opened at milestone dates in Evan's life – precious gifts that he, and I, will cherish always. She left gifts of advice, wisdom, memories and an infectious laugh that Evan has inherited directly from his mother. Hearing the two of them laugh in tandem is something that always brings a smile to my face.

We were back in the hospital for the second time within a week in early October. We didn't realize it yet, but this would be our last stay in the oncology wing. This is when we got the news that the chemotherapy was not working and that we were out of options for treatment.

We'd reached the end of the road.

After the immediate shock wore off, we started talking about our next steps. One of the decisions we reached was that Courtney would not die in the hospital; she would be discharged as soon as possible. Another was that she was going to reach out to close friends and family and give them the news herself. As usual, she was still taking charge and living life on her own terms.

During this time I sat in awe as I watched my wife do something I'd seen her do countless times, but didn't expect to see this time.

As we started making phone calls and letting our families know what was happening, I listened to my wife comfort and console others – lifting *their* spirits – as she broke the news. The trend continued as family and friends began arriving at the hospital. I watched with love and pride as she comforted not only me, but also our families and friends who came to see her.

As you can imagine, this was not a happy visit, but through it all I would hear her laugh and couldn't help but join in. Stories were told, memories shared, and it became more of a celebration of the life she'd led than a tearful farewell.

Court was a firm believer that cancer would never define her, but was just a part of her story. Cancer was not the story of Courtney. Cancer did add a sense of urgency to our lives and forced us to focus on the important things.

"Don't sweat the small stuff" took on a whole new meaning in our marriage and gave us a stronger bond and deeper love than I thought possible.

The women she met and friendships she formed with the "lifers" and others diagnosed with this disease are bonds that will never be broken. This is a group of women who will inspire even the toughest of us. They don't quit, they keep going, they take control of their lives, and they advocate for their health. One would think being diagnosed as "terminal" at the age of 33 would be the straw that would break anyone's back. How do you pick yourself back up after that? With Court and these women, it gave them a new appreciation and zest for life and for their families, friends and one another.

Cancer is a cruel disease and one that does not discriminate. Old, young, female, male – I'd wager that you personally know someone afflicted with cancer. According to the National Cancer Institute, roughly 38.5% of the population will develop some type of cancer in their lifetime. That's a shocking statistic, a sickening statistic, one that needs to be erased. It's a statistic that we as a society can drastically improve.

The five-year survival rate after being diagnosed with Stage 4 (metastatic) breast cancer is 22%, according to the American Cancer Society. That means approximately 78% of the women who are diagnosed as such will not survive beyond five years. Courtney fell into this category as she passed away three years to the month after recurring with metastatic breast cancer that settled in her liver. Despite these horrifying metrics, this group receives less than 10% of breast cancer research funds. These women deserve better.

Over the years, Courtney was passionate about and involved with multiple charities and organizations. She had a voice and she used it well. The Breast Cancer Resource Center, Metavivor, Theresa's Research Foundation, and the Noreen Frasier Foundation are all organizations she supported. As Courtney would say, we've reached a level where everyone is aware of cancer, now let's quit raising money for awareness and focus that money towards finding a cure.

Turn on your television this October – to watch a sporting event, parade, show or the news. There will be pink everywhere and more pleas for funding to "promote awareness" than at any other time of the year. Your contributions are key to eradicating this terrible disease.

But where are your donations going?

Are they to fund more awareness campaigns?

Do they have a pricey marketing program that eats up the majority of their funding?

How much money is actually earmarked towards research to find a cure?

These are questions that must be asked, and I hope you know the answer before you open your wallet.

I'll leave you with Courtney's favorite quote, one that's engraved on her tombstone: "Courage is not defined by those who fought and did not fall, but by those who fought and fell and rose again."

Courtney was an amazing wife, mother, daughter, sister and friend. *We love you, Court, and we know we'll see you again.*

Cancer industry is in need of reform

By Joe G. Bax,
Courtney's dad

Our daughter Courtney left us in the autumn of 2016, when she was 36. Cancer – that disease that had been so vicious, so unfair, that took control of her life and did everything to diminish her – at least gave her the opportunity to say good-bye.

Courtney, who focused her entire life on her family and friends, knew she was loved and treasured. She made the transition to Heaven with the same grace and ease that she always had in life.

Throughout her life, even as a small girl, she sought inspiration in the words of others. She loved to write, most often just for herself. She collected quotations. We would often find them at the bottom of an e-mail. Before the Internet, they could be found on her school work; sometimes they were just written alone on a scrap of paper. She was especially fond of quotations that spoke of courage – which, as it turned out, was a virtue she displayed in great abundance during the last five years of her life.

Clichés get used so frequently. They are readily quoted without the slightest bit of forethought. They are easy to grab and plug into whatever context presents itself. There is one cliché that was universally detested by Courtney and her breast cancer friends: "She lost her battle with breast cancer." These women are warriors with courage and grit. They do not lose battles. They are left scarred and dead because of so many reasons that we could easily control or, at a minimum, improve.

My wife Michele and I were ill-equipped to join our daughter in her fight. There was little cancer in the family. Courtney had five or six genetic tests. They showed no predisposition to cancer. But, you start reading. You ask questions and over some period of time, you develop a sense of the ebbs and flows of cancer and the ever-increasing cancer industry.

Dr. Google can give you a walking start, but you will graduate to research articles and books. My suspicions were confirmed when I read *The Emperor of All Maladies* by Siddhartha Mukherjee, M.D. Cancer research is an illogical cluster of mismatched efforts that, hopefully, will cure the most complex disease known to man. Maybe, and that is about as close as I can get, within the bureaucracies of the large research hospitals there is something that passes for a structured and logical approach with an ounce or two of organization behind it. Dr. Mukherjee suggests that any coordination between research behemoths dies a quick death due to pettiness and professional jealousies. Ignoring these human failings, the protective proprietary concerns of drug companies surround clinical trials in a fog of secrecy.

When you become a lab rat, you have exhausted your options. If they help you, that is great. If they hurt you, that is the risk assumed. Without some coordinated attack, women will continue to die.

Let's talk about breast cancer charities. Courtney's favorite charities were Metavivor, Theresa's Research Foundation, Noreen Frasier Foundation and Breast Cancer Research Center. We all understand fiscal responsibility. Certainly, we expect the executives of all charities to conduct their affairs in a sound businesslike manner.

That being said, can someone explain to me why breast cancer charities are sitting on billions, yes with a "b," of dollars of cash reserves. Their rainy day fund grows while these young women die and/or go broke awash in medical expenses. At one time, probably 30 or more years ago, we may have needed to raise the profile of this disease. Today one in eight women will develop breast cancer. No family skirts its impact. One cannot watch a newscast on a weekly basis without seeing a breast cancer story. You can wrap the entire National Football League in pink tape; it will not make us more aware. Awareness has reached the saturation point. In the meantime, funds are contributed with the best of intentions. But are they used to cure the disease?

Give that just a little thought. If you or I collected huge sums for a specific purpose and did not use them as represented, there would be dire consequences. Please do your own research and satisfy yourself that your contributed funds are quickly going to the cause that you intended.

Most of us learn how to prioritize our lives. Daily, we make decisions ranking one choice over another. Currently, the real "sizzle" in research is genetics. It garners the largest share of research dollars. Yet, only 5% to 10% of breast cancers are traceable to a genetic cause. Is this how you would prioritize your efforts? I suspect not; but there is no overarching logic to how the disease is attacked. We shall continue to lumber along, extending grants on a random basis. The best grant-request writers will receive the lion's share of the available funds – which may not be the best approach to finding a cure.

Courtney died of metastatic breast cancer, meaning that the cancer cells had left her breast and metastasized to another part of her body. If cancer remains confined to your breast, it will not kill you. People are often shocked to hear that. Conversely, if it leaves your breast, it becomes terminal. Metastatic breast cancer kills 99% of the time. Metastatic breast cancer receives between 7% to 9% of the breast cancer research dollars. I fail to see the logic.

Courtney had some great doctors, and some that fell below that standard. However, the entire system lacks any element of sensitivity. Her book contains some heart-wrenching examples, and she did not include them all. Courtney was dealing with a life-and-death situation. To some technician, it was just Tuesday. If someone is a boorish, ham-handed, insensitive klutz, wrapping them in a medical degree and a pair of scrubs will not change that. However, couldn't you code the oncology tests and expedite the effort? Do the results always have to come at 5 p.m. before a weekend? Many times, prior to a scan, I prayed, not for a specific result, but that Courtney would be able to handle the wait, the anxiety and the stress created by the system.

The stress of cancer is not just the fear of dying from the disease. It includes the fatigue of constantly being your own advocate. The system can't be depended on to move you along from station to station. The system is more likely to discard you, drop your file, or, in Courtney's case, lose your tumor block! Anonymous bureaucrats will render opinions that have mortal consequences. For example, metastatic breast cancer in your liver is not liver cancer. You may now have cancer in your liver, but it is not deemed to be liver cancer. Therefore, you do not qualify for a liver transplant.

The Family Leave Act permits mothers and fathers to take a certain amount of time off when they have a baby. Couples who adopt are included. They get to enjoy time off with their infant. Courtney used a gestational carrier. The implanted embryo was theirs. It was not an adoption in the classic sense. It was their child genetically. Someone deep in the bowels of some bureaucracy in Washington, D.C., decided she did not meet their qualifications. The Family Leave Act did not apply. Suffering the agony of breast cancer, she was denied the benefits granted every other couple. It was infuriating and belittling.

The medical and Washington bureaucracies are not the only road blocks to cancer patients. The insurance industry has its own set of hurdles. Pre-approval must be sought for just about everything, and timing gets critical. Courtney was fortunate that her employer, Taylor Morrison, provided a very good group health plan. Their carrier assigned a specific case worker to handle her issues. This idea was so novel that it was almost shocking.

Even as enlightened as they were, every bureaucracy has its own rules. If your doctor says that a certain treatment will not work, you cannot risk wasting time undergoing it because some faceless bureaucrat in your insurance bureaucracy wrote a rule that you must follow their arbitrary procedure. It is never mentioned, but every insurance company provides a right to appeal. You are fighting cancer. It does not play by any rules. Cancer patients are constantly fighting battles on many fronts simultaneously. Bureaucracies are slow-moving, insensitive monoliths. Do not expect them to be competent, sensitive or caring.

As I watched the stress build and compound, I urged Courtney to just delegate her medical care to the professionals. Fortunately, Courtney knew better and ignored me. Just about the time she would relax, someone would miss something, fail to do a test, or neglect the simplest step. Every great medical or nursing school has a bottom of the class. She was right: You must be vigilant. At the same time, how does someone become a nurse on an oncology floor and not know how to access a port? That failure started at a much higher place than the oncology ward.

I never met Courtney's oncologist, a lady by the name of Beth Hellerstedt. I grew to have great confidence in this woman. Courtney's vote of support should have sufficed. Courtney had seen enough doctors to be able to separate and sort them into nice little piles. Dr. Hellerstedt returned texts, e-mails and phone calls. Some of those calls were returned as late as 10 p.m. She made her rounds at 6 a.m. That makes for a very long day. All that being said, she was totally invested in Courtney's care and well-being. You cannot repay that kind of dedication.

* * * * *

For the last five years of Courtney's life, whenever given the chance, I buttonholed the fathers of young girls. Courtney was a daddy's girl. Her loss is staggering. The female side of the breast cancer audience hears a lot of the discussion. The males pick up bits and pieces. So, dads, husbands and brothers, this is for you.

In 1971, I was sitting in Dean A. A. White's class on product liability at the University of Houston Law School. We were studying the process of licensing the birth-control pill for sale to the public.

No drug was more anticipated. I learned that the pill was tested on a group of 60-plus women. I recall thinking then that was a very small number. After retiring and returning to my agrarian roots as a rancher, I realized that farmers and ranchers had been regulating the estrus cycle of cows, sheep, goats and horses for decades. The 60-plus women were just needed to adjust the dosage. There was one flaw in the concept. Domesticated animals are generally slaughtered. They do not live long enough for researchers to draw any long-range conclusions.

About this same time, my wife attended a symposium on the hormonal treatment of menopausal women. There was a panel of doctors. The first one stated that women would be ill-advised to use hormones for fear of the increased risk of cancer. He was never called on again. Having lost a daughter to breast cancer, you can only imagine how many conspiracy theories have been shared with me about why cancer has not been cured. I have not bought into them because I do not think the medical community has the smarts to create a conspiracy.

Men, I am not a doctor. Today, most insurance companies recommend that women start getting a mammogram at around age 45 to 50. Courtney was 36 when she died. If the female in your life starts taking the birth-control pill, she should immediately start having an annual mammogram, even if you have to pay for it. You must be proactive. Do not expect to get a straight answer from the cancer industry.

My 80-year-old aunt had never used birth control. Her doctor said that her bones were becoming brittle. (What's the surprise? She was 80!) He prescribed the pill because it was a cheap, available form of estrogen. It was also very potent. Within two years she had breast cancer.

I repeat, I am not a doctor, but logic does not escape me. Go to any cancer hospital anywhere and count the number of female patients under 40 years of age. Now, count the number of male patients under 40. You will be shocked. Something is going on and no one cares to hazard a guess. If there is a conspiracy, it is a conspiracy of silence.

The cancer industry is a part of our culture that is recklessly out of control. All participants are educated. Some are even well-intended. But, there is no logic. There is no coordination. Do not expect one group to be able to access all of your records. That is what is supposed to happen, but it never does. Courtney carried a bag full of her records, CDs and scans from hospital to hospital. But no hospital could ever read the CD of another. It would be a great benefit if they could.

It is desperately important that someone accompany the patient to every appointment. Far too many of these young women find themselves abandoned by their live-in boyfriends or by husbands who cannot stand the stress and strain. Bankruptcies are common. Difficult choices between treatment and child care are forced on these ladies. You would think that some of the more well-heeled breast cancer charities might provide some support, low-interest loans or other aids.

* * * * *

Courtney did not want to write this book. She felt it was a story that no one would want to read. If you have gotten this far, you have proven her wrong. She often said that she did not want to turn the oncologists into homeless people, but that she would sure like to put them out of business. She would never discourage anyone from seeking whatever remedies modern medicine might provide. She hoped that her observations and perceptions might be of assistance to the women who follow her.

As her dad, I hope that one day soon, the heartbroken and grieving parents, husbands, siblings and loved ones of these young women might corral the charity executives, the researchers, and the medical and insurance bureaucrats and demand some accountability, some explanation. I would like to look deep into their eyes to determine if there is a soul there at all – to determine if their motives are truly selfless or selfish. The funds are available. They have already been contributed. Cancer could be cured. It must be cured.

Shortly after Courtney's passing, while rummaging around some of her old papers, we found an untitled poem that she wrote in college. It expresses very well the way she felt about those closest to her. I gave it a title: "Courtney's Farewell."

Courtney's Farewell

When my time here is over
and all is said and done,
when the sand has dwindled down
and all my time is spent,
I'd want you to know,
how much I loved you –
how much you meant.

I'd want to say I'm sorry
for all I couldn't be
I'd apologize for all the heartache,
the sadness and the grief.
When tomorrow never comes,
I'd pray the whole world true,
that you knew how much you meant to me,
and I was a worthy friend to you.

So when the tears begin to trickle down,
when the water starts to fall,
when you pray you'd wake,
it was all a dream,

a dream you couldn't shake,
know everything I tried to do,
all my actions
all my efforts,
they were all for you.

I'd want you all to realize,
you were my faithful guide,
you taught me everything I know.
You were my heart, you were my eyes.

I worshipped the ground you walked on,
you made me who I am.
You were my soul, my hope, my joy –
my heart's constant beat,
and for what it is, I'm sorry,
for all I couldn't be.

But when my time is over,
when it all comes to an end,
I'd want you all to know,
you made me who I am.

– *Courtney Bax, age 19,*
April 22, 2000

Appendix 1

Coping with chemo

Chemotherapy sessions will never go down in the annals of modern medicine as "pleasant experiences." But I found several ways to make them more tolerable. Here are some of the things that worked for me:

Things that saved me:

1. Water
2. Sauna
3. Mineral baths
4. Exercise
5. Sleep
6. Exercise
7. Water

There's a theme here....

• First – **water, water, water!** I started chugging water the second I arrived at chemotherapy, and I try to drink at least 100 ounces per day. I downloaded a water app on my phone to track it.

When water starts to taste bad - which it will - I add those MiO bottles or Kool-Aid, lemon or Crystal Light to it, but I work to get in the 100 ounces of water *every day*, even on non-chemo days.

• Depending on the chemo, everything starts to taste bad. My mouth tastes sort of like cotton balls all the time and kind of chalky. There are some great **sugar-free gums** that taste great – some taste like those orange Dreamsicles; that was a winner. Anything citrus is a winner!

• When I have infusion chemo, I put a **mint** in my mouth before they access my port or do the saline flush. The saline tastes like burnt skunk. With the mint in my mouth, I can't taste it. This holds true with any scans, tests, etc. when they are going to do a saline flush first.

• It often hurts when they access my port, so I ask for some EMLA cream (a **topical anesthetic**) to apply 30 minutes before the procedure; it numbs everything. When they do the procedure right, I don't need it. However, I have learned not to expect it to be done correctly every time, so I usually apply the cream.

• When I feel burning around the port during chemo, I use a **hypoallergenic bandage** instead of the standard one. For whatever reason, the regular ones make it burn. (This is a tip from a chemo nurse; they have great tips. I tell them everything I am feeling. That's where the mint tip came from!) Oncology nurses regularly deal with the day-to-day effects of chemo; I use them as much as I can!

• I make sure to have a **companion** with me at chemo/radiation, and we try to have a little fun. But it's not fun. It sucks. Everything about cancer sucks, but we found it was better when we would try to enjoy ourselves. We got to where we knew everyone, and I'd just wheel myself around and talk to everyone. The nurses would have to come find me. It made the time go by faster.

• I didn't have any issues with nausea while on Taxol, but everyone is different; I know people who did. They made sure the pump was full of **anti-nausea drugs** at chemo, and that I had medicine at home. I would take one Ondansetron every morning, and then if I got nauseous during the day I would take this sublingual pill that dissolved and would take away any nausea. It was awesome.

• I have learned to be **careful of what I eat** at chemo. I no longer eat any of my favorite foods. One day I ate a sandwich at chemo. I didn't get sick, but to this day I cannot eat sandwiches because they taste like chemo. Same thing goes for all the little snacks they pass out; they all still taste like chemo. No more pretzels or vanilla crème cookies for me! Mention the word *sandwich, pretzel* or *cookie* and I get nauseous.

They told me not to worry about anti-cancer diets during chemo because I would need my energy. That being said, I don't know how it works for oral chemo, but all that starchy stuff has two effects:

1) I end up feeling bad or nauseous later because it's just too heavy and too much for the body to process (chemo plus bad food).

2) I end up gaining weight, which has the additional effect of also making me feel bad.

So, I don't diet, I don't worry about anti-cancer stuff, but I do try to eat fresh stuff. The only thing I can really eat after I wake up from my after-chemo nap is an apple and goat cheese. I also do a lot of berry smoothies in the morning for the antioxidants.

• I got myself some **low-dose Ambien** so I can sleep. I am mindful not to get addicted to it, but the body is healing during sleep and the chemo messes with my sleep. I use it only when I have to, but I do use it. That being said, for some reason the chemo makes me really light-sensitive at night. I bought a sleeping mask, but I found that even the light on the DVR wakes me up.

When I was given steroids with chemo, I tried to get them to wean me off it when I was doing okay. Steroids made me super-emotional.

• I am not afraid to **play the cancer card**. If I feel bad, I play it. The book *Crazy Sexy Cancer* talks a lot about this and it's pretty funny, too. Also, I have learned not to be afraid to say no to my friends and family. That is really hard, candidly. People want to visit me to show that they care, but all I really want sometimes is to vegetate at home. I make decisions with my best interest in mind. I learned that I will never need to put myself first more than I do now. It's time for me to be No. 1 with me.

• When my eyebrows started to thin, I went to Sephora and got the Makeup Forever **eyebrow pencil**. It stays on all day. The consultant matched my brows and showed me how to draw them on. No one believed me when I told them that my eyebrows fell out. I do the same thing for my eyelashes. I use a dark eye shadow and a brush to make the "smoky eye" look. This works so well that no one believes I lost all my lashes.

• Some people are wig people, some people are scarf people, some people are let-it-all-hang-out bald people. And for my newly bald head, I do what makes me feel comfortable and makes me feel good. I want to feel normal at work and not have people treat me like I'm sick, so **I wear wigs**. I didn't settle on just one wig. I got several of them and I love my wigs and wish my real hair could be as pretty! I also explored www.headcovers.com, a great site for scarves, hats, etc., and I got a lot of stuff from them. I e-mailed Good Wishes and received one scarf free. The site has gorgeous scarves, too. (http://www.goodwishesscarves.org). There really are tons of great scarves and hats out there.

• The last huge thing I do is **exercise**. I try to exercise every day that I'm not doing chemo. I don't overdo it; I know my limits. But I keep in mind that chemo kills red blood cells while exercise makes red blood cells, so I'm just trying to stay even. If I feel bad, I take a leisurely walk around the neighborhood. Often I'm spent, exhausted, when I get home, so I just go to bed. The fresh air makes me feel better, too.

• I also take **minerals baths** and sit in the **steam room** at the gym – anything to pull that chemo out!

• A note regarding my husband: Roger is going through this with me but he is also going through something totally different. He struggles with wanting to care for me and also worries about what will happen if things go south. I give him free nights to go blow off steam with his friends or with Evan. He doesn't want to leave my side because he feels guilty. On the days I feel good and don't need him, I give him a free pass to go play a round of golf or run errands or bury himself in work or whatever.

It's how he copes, because he will never cope in front of me. Roger doesn't confide in me about his fears or experience and is usually insistent that "everything is just fine." That in itself frustrates me thoroughly, but I know he's trying to protect me in his own way.

We eventually realized we needed to talk through how we wanted to handle this stress. Girls, I strongly suggest that you talk with your spouse or whoever is the main person in your support system. Clear communication is the key to keeping the frustration low – and you'll both be better off for it. Lord knows, there's more than enough stress in situations like ours without adding more to it, right?

Everyone copes differently. Everyone is walking blindly through this, and no one knows "the right thing to do." My suggestion is to just give people the benefit of the doubt; just because they aren't doing something the way you would do it doesn't mean they're not doing their best.

Hugs & Prayers...

Courtney

Playlist

Some of the songs that inspired and sustained Courtney in her
adult life...

"All My Trials" – Traditional folk song

"Beautiful Boy" – John Lennon
   (Words and music by John Lennon)

"Blackbird" – The Beatles
   (Words and music by John Lennon and Paul McCartney)

"Bottom of the Sea" – Sean McConnell
   (Words and music by Sean McConnell)

"Free Sailing" – Hoyt Axton
   (Words and music by Mark Dawson)

"Gonna Fly Now" – Theme song from *Rocky*
   (Words and music by Bill Conti, Carol Conners and Ayn Robbins)

"Have You Ever Seen the Rain?" – Creedence Clearwater Revival
   (Words and music by John Fogarty)

"Ironic – Alanis Morissette
   (Words and music by Alanis Morissette and Glen Ballard)

"Just Breathe" – Pearl Jam
   (Words and Music by Eddie Vedder)

"Kill a Word" – Eric Church
   (Words and music by Eric Church)

"Let It Be" – The Beatles
(Words and music by John Lennon and Paul McCartney)

"Like I'm Gonna Lose You" – Meghan Trainor
(Words and music by Caitlyn Elizabeth Smith, Justin Weaver and Meghan Trainor)

"Piece of My Heart" – Janis Joplin
(Words and music by Jerry Ragovoy and Bert Berns)

"Rise" – Eddie Vedder
(Words and music by Eddie Veder)

"Rise Up" – Audra Day
(Words and music by Cassandra Batie and Jennifer Decilveo)

"Save Some Time to Dream" – John Mellencamp
(Words and music by John Mellencamp)

"Shine On" – Sawyer Fredericks
(Words and music by May Erlewine)

"S.O.B." – Nathaniel Rateliff & the Night Sweats
(Words and music by Nathaniel Rateliff & the Night Sweats)

"Stubborn Love" – The Lumineers
(Words and music by Jeremy Fraite and Wesley Schultz)

"There's Always Something There to Remind Me" – Dionne Warwick
(Words and music by Burt Bacharach and Hal David)

"Tomorrow Never Comes" – Zac Brown
(Words and music by Zac Brown, Nico Moon and Wyatt Durrette)

"Trouble" – Ray LaMontagne
(Words and music by Ray LaMontagne)

"Turn the Page" – Bob Seger
(Words and music by Bob Seger)

"Wake Me Up" – Avicii
(Words and music by Tim Bergling, Aloe Blacc
and Michael Einziger)

"Weary Kind" – Ryan Bingham
(Words and music by Ryan Bingham and T-Bone Burnett)

"With a Little Help from My Friends" – Joe Cocker
(Words and music by John Lennon and Paul McCartney)

Index

Note: Page numbers in *italics* refer to photographs
or content within the captions of photographs.

About the Author

COURTNEY BAX LASATER (1980-2016) was a
wife, mother and author who was diagnosed with
breast cancer at age 30. Born in Houston, Texas,
she was a resident of Austin for most of her adult
life. She earned Bachelor's and Master's degrees
in marketing from Texas A&M University. In
an effort to help others with cancer, and as a
legacy to her son, she wrote a book recounting
her battle with the dreaded disease and what
she learned along the way. The book is titled
INFUSED: My Story of Cancer, Hope and Love.

Inspiring Books
from
Acadian House Publishing

Infused
My Story of Cancer, Hope and Love

A 208-page hardcover autobiography of a young Austin, Texas, woman and her 5-year battle with breast cancer. The narrative takes us from her original diagnosis (only 3 months after she was married) through her search for the right doctor, chemotherapy, mastectomies, and the birth of her child by way of a surrogate. Written in a lively and very informative voice, the story is infused with hope, inspiration, and wit, with an extra dose of sarcasm. (Author: Courtney Bax Lasater, ISBN 0-925417-21-1. Price $22.95)

Purses & Shoes For Sale
The Joys and Challenges of Caring for Elderly Parents

A 216-page book about the author's journey as a caregiver to her elderly parents in the twilight of their lives. Packed with suggestions on how to deal with issues encountered by adult children of the elderly. Includes a Q&A section with answers to frequently asked questions, plus a resources section with practical advice, useful websites and glossary of terms. (Author: Camille Pavy Claibourne. Harcover ISBN: 0-925417-96-3. Price: $17.95; Softcover ISBN: 0-925417-49-1. Price: $14.95)

Dying In God's Hands

A 152-page hardcover book that provides keen insights into the hearts and minds of the dying. It is based on a dozen or more interviews with terminally ill hospice patients, in which they share their hopes, dreams, fears and needs. The majority of the interviews provide evidence that faith in God and belief in the hereafter are the greatest strengths of the dying. Designed to comfort the dying and their loved ones, the book also contains a section of prayers and prose from all major world religions. (Author: Camille Pavy Claibourne. ISBN: 0-925417-64-5. Price: $16.95)

Freedom From Fear
A Way Through The Ways of Jesus The Christ

Everyone at one time or another feels fear, guilt, worry and shame. But when these emotions get out of control they can enslave a person, literally taking over his or her life. In this 142-page softcover book, the author suggests the way out of this bondage is prayer, meditation and faith in God and His promise of salvation. The author points to parables in the Gospels as Jesus' antidote to fears of various kinds. (Author: Francis Vanderwall. ISBN: 0-925417-34-3. Price: $14.95)

Waiting For Eli
A Father's Journey from Fear to Faith

A 176-page hardcover book about a Lafayette, La., couple and their infant son Eli who was born with a dreaded birth defect called *spina bifida*. It is an inspiring story of faith, hope and the power of prayer. The book has a strong pro-life, pro-love message, and is made even more compelling by the author's descriptions of little miracles along the way. (Author: Chad Judice. ISBN: 0-925417-65-3. Price: $16.95)

Eli's Reach
On the Value of Human Life and the Power of Prayer

Eli's Reach is the sequel to the inspiring, heartwarming book, *Waiting for Eli*, which tells the story of a Lafayette, La., couple and their child Eli, who was born with a birth defect called *spina bifida*. It is the story of how this child's life has touched the hearts and influenced the thinking of many. Hearing Eli's story has brought about a keener appreciation of the value of all human life and is credited with saving several unborn babies from abortion. (Author: Chad Judice. Hardcover ISBN: 0-925417-79-3. Price $16.95; Paperback ISBN: 0-925417-25-4, Price $14.95)

Getting Over the 4 Hurdles of Life

A 160-page hardcover book that shows us ways to get past the obstacles, or hurdles, that block our path to success, happiness and peace of mind. Four of the most common hurdles are: "I can't / You can't," past failures or fear of failure, handicaps, and lack of self-knowledge. This inspiring book – by one of the top motivational speakers in the U.S. – is brought to life by intriguing stories of various people who overcame life's hurdles. (Author: Coach Dale Brown. Hardcover ISBN: 0-925417-72-6. Price $17.95; Paperback ISBN: 0-925417-83-1, Price $14.95)

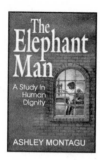

The Elephant Man
A Study in Human Dignity

A 138-page softcover book whose first edition inspired the movie and the Tony Award-winning play by the same name. This fascinating story, which has touched the hearts of readers throughout the world for over a century, is now complete with the publication of this, the Third Edition. Illustrated with photos and drawings of The Elephant Man. (Author: Ashley Montagu. ISBN: 0-925417-41-6. Price: $12.95.)

Dreaming Impossible Dreams
Reflections of an Entrepreneur

This 176-page autobiography is the rags-to-riches story of multimillionaire philanthropist E.J. Ourso of Donaldsonville, Louisiana, the man for whom the LSU Business School is named. It reveals how Ourso acquired 56 businesses in 48 years – the first 25 with no money down. A testament to the effectiveness of the American free enterprise system, the book chronicles Ourso's life beginning with his early years as a salesman. It reveals his secrets to the acquisition of wealth. (Author: E.J. Ourso with Dan Marin. Softcover ISBN: 0-925417-43-2. Price $16.95)

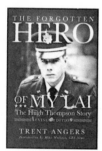

The Forgotten Hero of My Lai
The Hugh Thompson Story (Revised Edition)

The 272-page hardcover book that tells the story of the U.S. Army helicopter pilot who risked his life to rescue South Vietnamese civilians and to put a stop to the My Lai massacre during the Vietnam War in 1968. Revised Edition shows President Nixon initiated the effort to sabotage the My Lai massacre trials so no U.S. soldier would be convicted of a war crime. (Author: Trent Angers. ISBN: 0-925417-90-4. Price: $22.95)

TO ORDER, list the books you wish to purchase along with the corresponding cost of each. Add $4 per book for shipping & handling. Louisiana residents add 9% tax to the cost of the books. Mail your order and check or credit card authorization (VISA/MC/AmEx) to: Acadian House Publishing, Dept. INF, P.O. Box 52247, Lafayette, LA 70505. Or call (800) 850-8851. To order online, go to www.acadianhouse.com.